Starving to Live

Gateways to Counselling

Consultant editor:
Windy Dryden, Professor of Counselling at Goldsmiths
College, University of London

Series editor:
Maria Stasiak

Project manager:
Carron Staplehurst

The *Gateways to Counselling* series comprises books on various aspects of counselling theory and practice. Written with the assistance of the Central School of Counselling and Therapy, one of the largest counselling training organisations in the UK, the books address the needs of both students and tutors and are relevant for a range of training courses, regardless of specific orientation.

Other books in the series include:

AN INTRODUCTION TO CO-DEPENDENCY FOR COUNSELLORS
Gill Reeve

COUNSELLING SKILLS FOR PROFESSIONAL HELPERS
John Pratt

COUNSELLING IN A GENERAL PRACTICE SETTING
James Breese

ON LISTENING AND LEARNING
Student counselling in further and higher education
Colin Lago and Geraldine Shipton

TRANSCULTURAL COUNSELLING
Zack Eleftheriadou

STARVING TO LIVE
The paradox of anorexia nervosa

Alessandra Lemma-Wright

Central Book Publishing Ltd
London

First published 1994
by Central Book Publishing Ltd
Centre House, 56B Hale Lane
London, NW7 3PR

Typeset in 10 on 12 point Century Roman and Optima by
Intype, London.
Printed in Great Britain by
Tudor Printing, Park Road, Barnet

Cover illustration by Helen S. Roper

British Library Cataloguing in Publication Data

Lemma-Wright, Alessandra
   Starving to Live: Paradox of Anorexia
   Nervosa. – (Gateways to Counselling
   Series)
   I. Title II. Series
   616.85

ISBN 1–898458–15–4

To Cinzia

Contents

Introduction

USES AND ABUSES OF LABELS – SOME REFLECTIONS ON TERMINOLOGY

Those who express their difficulties and concerns through their relationship with food and their bodies have been called many things – anorectic, bulimic, bulimarectic, eating disordered, eating distressed and so on. The assumptions behind such labels are sadly overlooked and our unquestioning attitude towards the language we employ to describe the world and people in it has important implications. Labels and the information they contain influence to a great extent how we see and understand that which the label describes. In the case of the individual who self-starves, some labels, for instance, implicitly assume that the cause of their behaviour and distress is an 'illness' of some kind. This, in turn, determines how we approach the individual and how we define our roles and responsibilities as practitioners.

With the exception of the label 'patient' – which I believe reinforces the erroneous assumption that on the one hand there is a counsellor/therapist, healthy and strong, and on the other there is a 'patient', sick and weak – I have chosen in the pursuit of clarity to use the label 'anorectic', despite many misgivings. In Chapter 1 I trace the historical development of the concept of 'anorexia nervosa' through to current definitions and offer a working definition of anorexia for the purposes of this book. However, even though I have chosen to use the label 'anorectic' I urge the reader not to lose sight of the fact that labels obscure as much as they clarify.

ABOUT THE BOOK

There is no shortage of literature on anorexia and some of it is of a very high standard and informative. My aim in writing this book was thus not motivated by the desire to make a radically original contribution to the field. Rather it was influenced by a realisation that the wealth of literature that is available may be overwhelming for the newcomer to the field and, in particular, may not always be relevant to the needs of practising counsellors. Indeed a substantial proportion of the literature applies to work in in-patient settings and is laden with medical terminology. Chapters 2 and 3 of this book thus aim to provide a synthesis of recent research in the field as well as providing some basic facts on anorexia to enable counsellors to have some reference points.

The literature on anorexia contains a large number of papers and books which address a variety of factors assumed to be implicated in its aetiology. Equally, many papers have focused on the 'treatment' of anorexia. Far less common, however, are those writers who have attempted to offer a phenomenological insight into the world of the anorectic and thereby help us understand what it feels like for her to 'be-in-the-world'. Descriptive material which does not concern itself with the *why* of anorexia but rather attempts to address the *how* and *what* of the anorectic's experience would enable us to begin to appreciate the complex role that anorexia plays in the lives of its sufferers. The aim of Chapter 4 is to attempt to redress this imbalance through an existential analysis of anorexia. By way of illustration I refer in particular to the experiences of two women whom I have known in my capacity as a counsellor. I also refer to published autobiographical material by two women who have written about their personal experiences of anorexia.

Whilst it is important to stress that what these women have related of their sense of self and outlook on life pertains to them in a very personal way, striking similarities in their experience of 'being-in-the-world' can also be traced. These similarities in turn point to common starting points and aims in the anorectic's struggle.

The basic premise throughout this book is that counselling anorectics is not essentially different to counselling any other type of client. However, it does require some specialist knowledge and, more importantly, it may well *feel* different because of the nature of the problem. Chapter 5 addresses particular issues that counsellors may need to consider when working with anorexic clients. As well as offering some broad guidelines for 'good' practice based on the understanding of the anorectic's existential position described in Chapter 4, the reader is also invited to reflect at a more personal level on some of the issues raised in the chapter. Chapter 6 explores some of the dilemmas that counsellors may face in the course of their work, for instance in relation to the potentially life-threatening nature of anorexia.

The stance which I have adopted throughout the book is that it is important continually to challenge our assumptions and beliefs about the anorectic so that we may approach our client unencumbered, in so far as it is possible, by theoretical prejudices. We are nonetheless all construers of experience and continually develop theories about our own behaviour and that of others. As counsellors we are inevitably guided in our work by the theoretical systems we espouse. This book is not exempt from such biases.

I have chosen not to review every counselling approach to working with anorectics or to write the book from just one particular theoretical standpoint. Rather, I have attempted to distil guidelines for practice on the basis of my experience with this client group. Inevitably, my own theoretical allegiances have determined what I have chosen to emphasise and what I have left out. My understanding of the anorectic and how her needs can best be met within counselling has been largely influenced by my interest in existential ideas even though I am also indebted to the insights afforded by psychoanalytic ideas.

The existential approach to counselling is less about 'techniques' and more about an attitude towards counselling. In view of this it avoids many of the pitfalls of writing from other theoretical standpoints in that it does not prescribe particular techniques but invites us to consider our own personal philosophies. Their exploration helps us to clarify that which we believe to be our role and hence our aims in counselling the individual who self-starves.

I have also felt it important to address the book to practitioners in private as well as public health care settings. This is largely as a result of my own experiences as a counsellor, psychotherapist and clinical psychologist with this client group in both settings. The setting in which we work bears a direct relationship to how we are able to function as counsellors and makes specific demands on us. In particular, it raises a number of issues pertaining to our responsibilities as counsellors which become particularly pertinent when working with anorexic clients.

One final but important point is that whilst it is a well-established fact that more women than men develop anorexia, it is nonetheless important to remain cognisant of the findings that demonstrate that it does occur in men as well. Whilst we need to bear this in mind I will use feminine nouns and pronouns throughout this book when referring to sufferers unless otherwise specified.

Parts of Chapter 4 first appeared in *Changes*, vol. 10(3) (September 1992), and are reproduced with kind permission of the publishers, Lawrence Erlbaum Associates.

1

Anorexia Through the Ages

'I always wanted you to admire my fasting', said the hunger artist. 'We do admire it', said the overseer affably. 'But you shouldn't admire it' ... 'But why shouldn't we admire it?' ... 'Because I have to fast, I can't help it' ... 'And why can't you help it?' ... 'Because', said the hunger artist, lifting his head and speaking with his lips pursed as if for a kiss, right into the overseer's ear, so that no syllable might be lost, 'Because I couldn't find the food I liked. If I had found it, believe me, I should have made no fuss and stuffed myself like you or anyone else'.

(Kafka, *The Hunger Artist*)

EARLY DESCRIPTIONS

The above words were the hunger artist's last words before he died. Until then he had lived most of his life in a cage where people could go to observe his skeleton-like figure. By the nineteenth century the public feats of such hunger artists became very popular in Europe and in the United States. While we no longer have hunger artists to capture our attention, in a manner akin to the nineteenth century's fascination with the hunger artist, we are now curious about the anorectic and her angular shape. Do we not stare if we meet someone who is extremely thin? Her emaciated body attracts our attention and we can't help but stare, sometimes in awe, sometimes in horror, and sometimes wondering why anyone should starve themselves amidst plenty.

At a time when the statistics for Europe and the United States indicate an increased incidence of anorexia, it may be timely to stop and consider the nature of anorexia, as it reflects so many of the moral, scientific and social problems and dilemmas that face us towards the end of the twentieth century. Our attempts to understand the phenomena that confront us are however made difficult by the fact that controlling and losing weight are behaviours which embody some of our western culture's most cherished values.

Anorexia is an 'illness' with great dramatic appeal, whose impact stretches far back into history, evoking images of ascetics and martyrs. Today the drama is played out in a society seduced by the angular. Even though the last twenty years have witnessed an increasing interest in 'eating problems' generally, anorexia is certainly not a new problem – not simply a result of the contradictory position of women in the latter half of the twentieth century. Indeed, while anorexia has only been identified as a psychiatric illness for just over one hundred years, the practice of self-starvation within a religious context has existed for much longer and continues to be practised by certain religious groups.

Brumberg (1988) has documented the historical roots of anorexia. She shows that accounts of self-induced weight loss, characteristic of anorexia, can be traced back to the Middle Ages. In medieval Europe, particularly in the years between 1200 and 1500, a small but significant minority of women refused their food and prolonged fasting was considered a 'female miracle'. Fasting was then understood as a fundamental expression of female holiness.

History chronicles the experiences of women – many of whom were later sanctified by the Church – who ate very little. Amongst the most notorious 'holy anorexics' (Bell 1985) is Catherine of Siena (1347–80) who, we are told, consumed only a handful of herbs and some fruit each day and who also occasionally pushed twigs down her throat to bring up any food that she may have otherwise been forced to eat. Bell has drawn some striking parallels between the 'holy anorexics' and contemporary anorectics, highlighting how many started their self-starvation in adolescence, typically in order to resolve some acute sense of self-doubt and unworthiness. However, such views are not shared by everyone and there are those who would argue that the medieval fasting women did not experience something analogous to what we now refer to as anorexia. While such debates are of theoretical interest they have little bearing on what we do when we are faced with someone who refuses to eat. It is nonetheless important to have a sense of perspective as history suggests that anorexia is not an exclusively modern problem. Rather it would appear that both food and the human body have been used, by women in particular, throughout the centuries as the focus of their symbolic language.

By the end of the seventeenth century the phenomenon of food abstinence started to draw the attention of physicians who variously labelled it 'inedia prodigiosa' (a great starvation) and 'anorexia mirabilis' (miraculously inspired loss of appetite). It is of interest that both these labels are still strongly evocative of something mystical and holy even though food abstinence had by then entered medical consciousness.

The first clinical description of anorexia was provided in 1694 by Richard Morton, an English physician, who reported two cases of a 'wasting disease' of nervous origin. Morton was particularly struck by what he saw, and wrote: 'I do not remember that I did ever in all my practice see one that was conversant with the living so much wasted.' Indeed he reported that one of his patients, 'a skeleton only clad in skin', died from 'a multitude of cares and passions of the mind'. This last statement is important because it represents the first clear association between self-starvation and psychological factors. Morton was also the first to report a case of anorexia in a man.

In the 1870s anorexia emerged clearly as a new 'disease' and in many ways reflected medicine's increasing sophistication in diagnosis. While the term 'anorexia nervosa' itself is said to have been introduced into the British medical literature around this time by Sir William Gull, there is some dispute as to whether it was in fact the French physician, Charles Lasegue, who first introduced the term. As with many such disputes, the reading of the French literature strongly favours Lasegue, while the English literature favours Gull – a sober reminder that the spirit of Chauvin was, and still is, alive on both sides of the Channel!

The nineteenth century's descriptions of anorexia strongly implicated sexual problems as a potential aetiological factor. The medical literature throughout this period contained a number of descriptions of women with amenorrhea (cessation of menstruation – an important diagnostic indicator of anorexia). An underlying assumption in such writings was that strong emotional reactions – particularly regarding sexual matters – might lead to menstrual disturbance. The cessation of menstruation was also believed to be a possible cause of mental disturbance – a syndrome known as menstrual insanity. Despite the renowned preoccupation of Victorian society with sexuality, William Gull's first description of anorexia made no mention of sexual development as related to its aetiology. Lasegue, however, saw it clearly as a variant of hysteria, and sexual problems assumed a prominent role in his understanding of anorexia.

As with most problems thought to be related to a psychological precipitant, Sigmund Freud also had something to say about anorexia, even though it only received a comparatively passing reference in his work. Despite this, his remarks nonetheless had a powerful influence on subsequent interpretations of anorexia.

Freud (1895) implicated a specific psychodynamic mechanism in the aetiology of anorexia and suggested a very clear link between loss of appetite and sexuality. According to Freudian theory all appetites were believed to be expressions of 'libido', that is, the sexual drive. Thus it was suggested that eating or not eating indicated the presence and expression, or absence, of basic sexual drives. Freud believed that the anorectic did not eat because food and sex revolted her. But why should this be so? In order to account for this he hypothesised that because of a prior association, food had assumed a symbolic significance which in turn made it repugnant. Freud's reading of anorexia as a neurotic behaviour that expressed undeveloped or repressed sexuality was grounded in his important concept of 'conversion hysteria' – that is, the belief that emotional conflicts can be transformed into physical symptoms.

Thus Freud suggestively linked anorexia to psychosexual development. Taken together with the prevailing concerns of Victorian society about issues of sexuality, such views gave substance to the emerging psychogenic idea that anorexic girls refused food in order to keep their bodies small and thin, thereby forestalling adult sexuality.

During the 1930s anorexia was clearly established as a female psychological 'disorder'. Perhaps not surprisingly, psy-

chiatrists following Freud readily postulated that the anorectic's refusal to eat was in some way linked with sexual problems.

From 1940 onwards until the early 1960s, psychotherapists
and psychiatrists simply continued to confirm that the anorectic experienced numerous conflicts around her sexuality, and
populated her fantasy world with sexual content, suggesting
that she feared eating as impregnation and regarded obesity
as pregnancy.

Psychoanalytic writers in particular crystallised the notion
of a psychosexual dysfunction in anorexia, suggesting that
such symptoms as amenorrhea and constipation were respectively linked to an unconscious wish to be pregnant and to a
wish to retain the baby (Waller *et al.* 1940). Anorectics began
to be seen as essentially sexually repressed or puritanical
individuals. Numerous accounts suggest that they were
embarrassed by vulgar stories, that they preferred reading to
going out with boys (strongly suggestive of a sexually repressed
individual, of course!), claimed never to masturbate and were
easily traumatised by unsolicited overtures from members of
the opposite sex. Allegedly, they feared that they could become
pregnant from male sperm residue left on chairs or refused
'slimy' foods because they associated these with semen.

While no one explicitly suggested that the anorectic's apparent refusal to reach full sexual maturity was an indication
that she was a lesbian, her 'childlike' body was undoubtably
interpreted as a repudiation of heterosexuality. As Brumberg
has suggested, this is likely to have touched a raw nerve in
the inter-war years, a time when a women's role was clearly
defined as one of 'reproduction'.

However, psychosexual dysfunction was by no means the
whole story. Anorectics were also portrayed as hysterically
exhibitionistic and seductive. Goiten (1942) suggested in no
uncertain terms that the anorectic was a potential prostitute,
whose lack of appetite was an unconscious defence against
promiscuity. Others claimed that the anorectic wanted to be
force-fed because of fellatio fantasies. While such descriptions
of the alleged fears and preoccupations of the anorectic are of
interest it is likely that such accounts reveal more about the
fantasies and preoccupations of the male professionals who
reported such accounts than those of the anorectic.

Once the link between anorexia and psychosexual development became fixed in the minds of those, predominantly male, professionals who were studying and treating anorectics, it very much determined what they chose to ask their anorexic patients in the therapeutic interview. This clearly meant that very little else was asked so that other areas of concern and conflict are likely to have been left unexplored.

ANOREXIA NERVOSA IN THE 1990s

Anorexia is currently reported to be on the increase. It is most probably true that as in the case of many 'disorders' the reported increase in cases of anorexia is to some extent due to heightened awareness and reporting on the part of families and doctors. If a professional is now faced with a girl or a woman with erratic eating habits and a preoccupation with weight, who also reports that her periods have ceased, it is likely that this will alert the professional to the possibility of anorexia.

The diagnosis of anorexia is not, however, a simple matter and there is considerable controversy as to how one defines it. The term itself is in many ways inappropriate as it implies that anorexia is rooted in a 'nervous loss of appetite'. This in turn suggests a loss of interest in, and desire for, food. However, those who have become anorexic report having a strong interest in food. More importantly, they feel that their appetite is too powerful and they attempt to control it by exerting constant vigilance and observing the most rigid rules about what they may or may not eat. The sufferers feel that if their control lapsed, even momentarily, and they ate food beyond their pre-established daily allowance, they would either lose control or 'go to pieces'.

The above observations have led some clinicians to point out that it is the preoccupation with weight control and the all-pervasive fear of weight gain which represent the most important and most characteristic symptoms of anorexia. Such definitions of anorexia are largely the result of an acknowledgement amongst clinicians of the need to differentiate between an unspecific refusal to eat and primary anorexia nervosa. Loss of appetite is a common symptom of many conditions such as depression and influenza. However, throughout this book we will concern ourselves with primary anorexia nervosa, commonly further divided into two sub-types, namely 'restrictive anorectics' and 'bulimic anorectics'. The former drastically cut back on their food intake, while the latter alternate strict dieting with binging and purging.

While some psychiatric diagnostic definitions of anorexia specify as one of their criteria the loss of 15 per cent or 25 per cent of original body weight, this may not be a particularly useful criterion because it renders the definition arbitrarily restrictive and has implications for intervention. If an individual values thinness to the extent that she starts severely restricting her food intake and she places a lot of value on keeping control of her eating, then how important is it whether she has 'only' lost a few pounds or has lost two stone? In both instances she is experiencing difficulty, is in distress and needs help. In this book therefore I shall be using the term 'anorectic' to denote someone with a central preoccupation with controlling her weight and so avoiding weight gain. The use of the term 'anorectic' will thus be independent of the indvidual's actual weight; rather it will apply to the way a person thinks and feels about herself in relation to her weight. The implication of this definition is that it encompasses the experiences of many women, who while not appearing severely emaciated, nonetheless find a way of coping with conflicts in their lives through the control of their weight.

DISCUSSION ISSUES

1   To what extent is it possible to understand eating problems without considering their historical and cultural context?

2

Some Basic Facts About Anorexia

WHAT IS ANOREXIA NERVOSA?

As we saw in Chapter 1, the definition of anorexia nervosa differs depending on which source one turns to. However, some diagnostic criteria do overlap and there is now considerable consensus over the main features. Anorexia is most typically diagnosed when the following criteria are met:

1 the individual refuses to maintain a body weight over a minimum 'Average Expected Body Weight' (AEBW) calculated on the basis of age, sex and height;

2 there is a disturbance in the way in which the individual's body weight, size or shape is experienced – for instance, the person claiming to feel fat even when emaciated or believing that one area of the body is too fat even when clearly underweight;

3 the individual experiences an intense fear of gaining weight or becoming 'fat' even though s/he is actually underweight;

4 in women, the absence of at least three consecutive menstrual cycles when otherwise expected to occur.

Similarities between anorexia and bulimia

In recent years, anorexia has been recognised as one of a group of probably related and overlapping 'disorders' of eating, alongside those conditions which have been variously termed 'bulimia', 'bulimarexia' and 'bulimia nervosa'. However, there is considerable dispute about the diagnostic criteria to be applied to this group of clients and this has complicated the attempts of researchers to study them.

Bulimia nervosa – 'bulimia' literally meaning 'ox hunger' – is a much more recent clinical concept. Towards the end of the 1970s there was an increasing recognition of the experiences of a group of people who fluctuated between periods of self-starvation and periods of uncontrolled eating. Although such individuals resembled those with anorexia in many ways, they were generally of normal weight. The patients Russell (1979) diagnosed as suffering from bulimia nervosa, for instance, all had powerful and intractable urges to overeat, yet were morbidly afraid of becoming fat and sought to avoid the fattening effects of food by inducing vomiting and abusing laxatives. Most had experienced an episode of anorexia. An individual is likely to be diagnosed 'bulimic' if they report recurrent episodes of binge eating (rapid consumption of food in a discrete period of time) and a feeling of lack of control over their eating behaviour during the binges. The person will also typically engage in regular self-induced vomiting, use of laxatives or duretics, strict dieting or fasting, or vigorous exercise in order to prevent weight gain.

On the whole researchers have felt it important to distinguish bulimia from anorexia, thereby singling out the former as a 'disorder' in its own right with very specific dynamics. For instance, it has been argued that by defining the bulimic as a 'sort of anorexic' we fail to appreciate the specific dynamics that are symbolised by the bulimic symptomatology whereby the taking in and then rejecting of food singles bulimia out as entirely different from anorexia. Others, however, have been more reluctant to differentiate between the two groups. The main difference they point to is the effectiveness with which the anorectic, as opposed to the bulimic, achieves weight loss.

Perhaps more significantly, there do not appear to be any clear-cut differences in the thinking and the goals of anorectics and bulimics. When listening to the stories of individuals who have been diagnosed anorexic and bulimic respectively it is the similarities rather than the differences between their experiences which are most striking. They both tend to make very similar statements about themselves and the world they inhabit. For both of them, food and weight control have become central preoccupations. Furthermore, about half of those with a diagnosis of anorexia alternate between episodes of dietary restraint and bulimic episodes.

Whilst it is important to recognise the similarities between anorexia and bulimia, there is little doubt that the bulimic and the anorexic symptoms respectively are partly determined by an individual's personal history. In this respect the 'choice' of symptoms may be meaningful and worthy of exploration in counselling. For instance, research suggests that bulimic symptoms in particular are associated with a previous experience of sexual abuse. There are also specific difficulties, both physical and psychological, that pertain to those individuals who binge and purge. Indeed the distress experienced by such individuals has been exacerbated by society's negative attitude to the binge/purge cycle, as this means of controlling one's weight appears to be far less socially acceptable, and certainly less admirable, than the classic anorexic stance.

Unlike the anorectic who embodies our culture's concern with control, the bulimic is someone whose behaviour encapsulates our fear of being out of control. She eats in a frenzy whatever she can lay her hands on. She may even start shoplifting, stealing food. Such behaviours elicit negative judgements. Nonetheless people tend to be fascinated by her behaviour and as with the anorectic, can be voyeuristic about such excesses – after all we are often most fascinated by that which we fear and which we cannot accept in ourselves. However, despite our curiosity we have no wish to be like the bulimic. The image of someone kneeling in front of the toilet and inducing vomiting is one from which we recoil and wish not to associate ourselves with. Such prevailing attitudes have undoubtedly contributed to the secrecy that often surrounds bulimic episodes and have thus prevented people from seeking help sooner.

Although this book focuses specifically on anorexia I will nonetheless be referring to individuals who alternate between anorexia and bulimic symptoms. I use these terms descriptively rather than diagnostically.

The role of 'overvalued ideas' in anorexia

A central feature of anorexia is that which is referred to as 'overvalued ideas' concerning the importance of shape and weight. In such instances the individual's belief in an idea is seen to be more 'emotional' than 'rational'. In the case of the anorectic she does indeed attach a great deal of importance to the pursuit of a thin body shape and the success of this pursuit often determines how she will feel about herself and her life. Cognitive counsellors and researchers have gone as far as to argue that the anorectic's 'overvalued ideas' concerning shape and weight constitute the core psychological disturbance in anorexia and that the main aim of treatment is to alter the individual's beliefs regarding the importance of shape and weight. Whilst it is debatable as to whether this is indeed the core problem it nonetheless remains true that one of the tasks of counselling is to facilitate the individual's exploration of her beliefs and assumptions regarding weight gain and control and how these relate to her sense of self.

Do anorectics overestimate their body size?

Researchers' attention has been drawn to the frequently observed discrepancy between the anorectic's perception of her body size and her actual body size. Consequently much research has been devoted to establishing whether the anorectic actually overestimates her body size. Indeed anorectics, as well as those differentially diagnosed as bulimic, have been found to overestimate their size when compared with individuals who are not anorexic or bulimic. However, many anorectics have also been found to be accurate in their estimations. Furthermore, many people with no eating problems also overestimate their size, suggesting that current cultural norms for what is thin and what is fat may have an insidious effect on how we all perceive our bodies, irrespective of whether we are anorexic or not. This is a very important point for it serves to remind us that while the anorectic's perception of her body may initially strike us as 'distorted' and may thus lead us to believe that she is 'sick' and different from us, we perhaps need to pause and consider how her attitudes towards her body and her perception of her body size show remarkable similarity with the experiences of many women whom we would not otherwise regard as 'sick'.

ARE ANORECTICS DEPRESSED?

Two assumptions that permeate the literature on anorexia are, on the one hand, that anorexia is simply one further manifestation of an 'affective disorder' such as depression or anxiety and, on the other hand, that anorexia occurs along with other problems such as anxiety, depression, substance abuse or 'personality disorder'.

The distinction, or lack of distinction, between anorexia and depression in particular has in the past been a contentious issue. Several studies have reported a family history of depression or anxiety in those who later become anorexic. Commonly, anorectics have also been found to have a personal history of depression. An important limitation of such research is that while the evidence does suggest a correlation between depression and anorexia, the chronology of the 'symptoms' is not always clear – that is, it is not possible to ascertain whether the depression is the result of the eating problem or vice versa. Nonetheless, such research does suggest that when working with someone who is anorexic we are likely to encounter a number of problems and that these will not just be problems around weight and body shape.

While some of us may not subscribe to the psychiatric classificatory system and would therefore not be too concerned with whether anorexia is really a form of depression or not, such issues are mentioned here for two reasons. Firstly, as counsellors working within National Health Service settings it is likely that we will be working alongside other professionals who hold such views. If we wish to criticise them for straightjacketing individuals into psychiatric categories it helps if we understand their language and are acquainted with the research. Informed criticism has a greater sting! Secondly, it is because eating problems generally have been believed to be a form of 'affective disorder' that medication is sometimes prescribed – the medication in question being anti-depressants. However, it is not very clear what the anti-depressants are supposed to be 'treating' when they are prescribed to someone who is anorexic. Indeed, there seems to be very little evidence to support the use of medication in anorexia. There is more convincing evidence however for their use with those individuals who are bulimic. A lively controversy exists as to whether the anti-depressants serve in such cases as anti-binge agents or rather are acting as an antidote for the depressive feelings that clients often report as triggers to the binging episodes. Although many questions with regard to the use of medication remain unanswered one thing seems clear: medication is neither a sufficient, nor a necessary, part of the treatment we should be offering someone who is anorexic.

ANOREXIA AND SEXUAL ABUSE

As we saw earlier in Chapter 1, the presence of sexual conflicts in anorectics has been well documented and perhaps, at times, unnecessarily emphasised. The emphasis has been in particular on the sexual *phantasies* of anorectics rather than on actual sexually traumatic experiences either as children or as adults. This bias has often meant that the anorectic is depicted as someone unable to cope with their emerging sexuality. By becoming anorexic, it is argued, the individual postpones having to deal with such issues by maintaining her body at a pre-pubertal stage of development.

One idea which has however received less attention is the possibility that by becoming anorexic the individual has found a way of dealing with a sexually traumatic experience in the past. For instance, one anorexic client who had also been sexually abused as a child viewed her body as a foreign container of her 'bad' sexual feelings and believed that by starving herself she could gradually get rid of the latter and thus purify herself. By denying her being as a 'being-in-a-body', she had found a solution to her earlier trauma.

Actual instances of sexual trauma or incest in the lives of those who have become anorexic have, until recently, been generally neglected. However, there are now several studies which have documented instances of child sexual abuse (CSA), as well as rape incidents, in individuals with an eating problem. One study reported that 30 per cent of clients referred to an eating problems clinic also had a history of CSA (McLelland *et al.* 1991). Such figures are quite common, with some studies reporting figures of up to 42 per cent. When considering such studies it is important to bear in mind that some of the variation in the percentages obtained is, at least in part, due to differences in the definitions of 'sexual abuse' used by the researchers.

Because not all sexually traumatised individuals develop an eating problem, and because some individuals with eating problems have not experienced sexual trauma, it is clear that sexual abuse or incest are neither necessary nor sufficient triggers for the emergence of anorexia. However, those who have suffered such abuse may represent a particularly vulnerable population and the emergence of an eating problem in a young girl or boy may alert us to the possibility of abuse. While not encouraging counsellors always to pursue this particular line in their work, it is important to be cognisant of the reported association between sexual abuse and anorexia so that we may be more likely to hear what is often, for many of us, something very difficult to hear.

THE PHYSICAL FEATURES OF ANOREXIA

Anorexia has attracted a great deal of attention both in and out of the medical profession. Physicians' focus on the anorectic's body is not surprising as anorexia is typically accompanied by characteristic physiological changes. The prevailing medical opinion is that the anorectic's physical symptoms at low weight are those of a healthy person whose body is adjusting to the effects of persistent undernutrition. There is therefore nothing mysterious about what we may observe happening to the anorectic's body: it is what would happen to us if we did not eat over an extended period of time. The threshold where emaciation becomes physically dangerous is reached when a person's weight falls between 60–5 per cent of AEBW. The speed with which the weight has been lost will also make a difference. If you are working with someone who is losing weight very rapidly she is more likely to be in immediate physical danger than someone who loses weight over an extended period of time, as the latter allows the body more time to adapt to the changes.

Physiological consequences of starvation, binging and self-induced vomiting

There are a number of typical physiological consequences associated with prolonged starvation. These are mentioned not because I wish to emphasise the physical aspects of anorexia to the exclusion of the psychological ones, but simply because their consequences have implications for counselling.

The literature on anorexia sways from those accounts which speak of anorexia as a purely psychological problem and pay very little attention to what is happening to the anorectic's body, to those books and articles which tend to focus a lot on the physical aspects and which subscribe to the view that unless the anorectic's body has been restored to its normal weight no psychological help can be used by the individual. Such positions represent extremes which fail to take into account the actual bodily *and* psychological experiences of the anorectic. To deny what is happening to the anorectic's body may be to collude with her position which is one, as I will argue in Chapter 4, which attempts to deny her being as a 'being-in-a-body'. Nonetheless, we must never lose sight of an important point: no matter how emaciated an individual is, she is always more than just a body and the help we offer her should be mindful of this fact.

The box below summarises the main physical complications associated with prolonged starvation. It is important to be aware of these factors, particularly if you are working outside of a medical setting, since if weight loss has been extreme, hospitalisation may be required in order to save a life. Anorexia has a fatal outcome in 5–10 per cent of diagnosed cases – a rate higher than that for any other psychiatric disorder. This raises difficult ethical dilemmas for the counsellor and we shall address these later in Chapter 6.

It is helpful to discuss with your client as openly as possible the ways in which they control their weight. If your client self-starves but also binges and abuses laxatives and/or induces self-vomiting, further physical complications will arise. Such methods of weight control are more dangerous than self-starvation from a medical point of view and your client may be in a precarious physical state due to electrolyte imbalance which, if extreme, can also lead to death. Metabolic disturbances, especially hypokaleamia (i.e. low potassium levels) are commonly associated with self-induced vomiting and purgative abuse and this can lead the individual to feel generally weak. Renal damage resulting from dehydration and electrolyte imbalance may also occur. In those cases where the electrolyte imbalance is very severe, the individual may also suffer from epileptic seizures. On the whole the physical complications associated with binging and purging are all reversible. This is with the exception of dental enamel erosion due to the loss of calcium which is associated specifically with self-induced vomiting.

Physical complications associated with starvation

1   Amenorrhea – cessation of menstruation

2   Bradycardia – slowing down of heart rate

3   Hypothermia – lowered body temperature

4   Hypertension – raised blood pressure

5   Gastro-intestinal disturbance

6   Abdominal pains

7   Lanugo – appearance of fine body hair

While some clients may be initially reluctant to admit to binging and vomiting, as such behaviours are often accompanied by feelings of shame and self-disgust, others will be relieved to be able to share their secret activity and not to feel rejected once they have told you.

By the time your client has fallen to 75 per cent of AEBW the classic physical picture of anorexia begins to emerge. Overall the rate of her metabolism slows down. The individual will begin to look very obviously frail. Her shoulder-blades, cheek bones, collar and hip bones will be more prominent. She will appear pale. Her arms, legs and extremities may turn a bluish colour due to a reduction in the volume of blood circulating in them. She will be cold to the touch. Her body will start showing the growth of fine body hair known as 'lanugo'. By this time she will also be starting to experience the discomforts of low weight. She may start wrapping herself in layers of clothes not only so as to hide her angular shape, but also because she will feel cold. Her protruding bones will make it uncomfortable for her to sit on hard surfaces for prolonged periods of time.

The anorectic's response to the experience of starvation

While it may be difficult for us to envisage how an individual who looks so frail and whose life seems to have become increasingly restricted could wish to continue on the path of self-starvation, we must not lose sight of the anorectic's reality. It is crucial for any therapeutic work to take place that we meet the anorectic where she is at any given weight. We need to acknowledge what she says and even if her statements may seem to us to be extreme, we need to accept them nonetheless as accurate and real perceptions for her of her situation. She will often be speaking from a position where her perspectives are extreme and where she may feel polarised. In such a place her perpetual feelings of coldness and her protruding bones may horrify us but serve to remind the anorectic that she is in control, that this is the one thing no one can take away from her. It is when her weight is increased, if she is in a hospital, that she will begin to really feel 'bad' and may actually want to die. Suicide is the most common form of death amongst anorectics who die prematurely. Tragically at times, our perceived attempts to keep her alive may in some cases precipitate the individual in taking her own life as she may feel that that which was keeping her alive has now been removed from her sphere of control.

Psychological effects of starvation

Some researchers have argued that many of the features of the anorectic's so-called 'psychopathology' could be a direct result of starvation. Thus it is argued that starvation leads to changes in the way people think. The way starvation is said to impair intellectual functioning is by progressively decreasing the individual's capacity for complex thought. Starving people are said to have fewer and fewer categories in which to place their experiences and this hypothesis is invoked to explain the typically black-and-white, polarised thinking of the anorectic.

The ability to concentrate has also been found to decrease as weight falls. Indeed it is not uncommon for anorectics to report that they experience difficulty reading or studying for extended periods of time.

Sexual feelings are also said to diminish when food intake is consistently reduced over long periods of time. The latter finding is frequently invoked to explain how, by reducing their sexual drive through starvation, individuals can temporarily resolve their sexual conflicts.

Starvation also induces a state of euphoria. This experience is also known as the 'fasting high' with which some of us may be familiar if we have gone without eating for a period of time. This is quite a normal reaction and occurs when people consistently cut back on the amount of food they eat. Depending on an individual's weight and the extent to which they have reduced their intake of food, such a change can begin to take place quite rapidly, for instance within as little as 24–48 hours.

The idea that these commonly observed features of anorexia as outlined above are the consequences of starvation is based on an experimental study of the effects of starvation conducted by Keys and colleagues in 1950. Male volunteers underwent semi-starvation, losing about 23 per cent of body weight. As the weight loss progressed the men began to think incessantly about food and were preoccupied with food-related activities, spending large amounts of time planning how and what to eat. They tended either to gulp their food or hoard it and eat it in small bites. Often they became asocial and quite reclusive. They reported significant impairments in their concentration as well as depressed mood.

Many of the experiences that the male volunteers underwent are also frequently reported by anorexic clients. However, while such research is of interest and it may prove useful to separate out the non-specific effects of starvation, we are not yet in a position to say with any certainty whether there is a causal link between such experiences and starvation. Moreover, it has not yet been satisfyingly demonstrated that such symptoms can be reversed by simply restoring body weight. Until such a time we must proceed with caution and not explain away our clients' experiences simply in terms of the effects of starvation.

DISCUSSION ISSUES

1 Under what conditions, if any, could you justify not involving medical help if your client was losing weight very rapidly?

2 Have you ever gone without food for a prolonged period of time? If so, what effects did this have on you (physically and psychologically)?

3

The Who and Why of Anorexia

WHO BECOMES ANOREXIC? – CHALLENGING THE STEREOTYPES

Over the years a number of factors have been associated with anorexia with remarkable consistency. The research which has brought such factors to light falls within a branch of medical science called epidemiology. The following factors have shown the most significant correlations with anorexia.

Age and gender

Both age and gender have consistently emerged as important factors. The vast majority of cases of anorexia are female and this is an important social characteristic of the anorexic population. The observed gender skew has attracted a great deal of attention and is the particular focus of socio-cultural explanations of anorexia. However, this fact has perhaps led to an overemphasis on anorexia as a 'female problem' and, as we will see later in this chapter, anorexia is not an exclusively female problem.

In general, most cases of primary anorexia nervosa tend to occur after the onset of puberty and before the menopause. The modal age of onset is 16. However there are exceptions to this. Although the incidence for younger, pre-pubertal children is not known there is a suggestion that anorexia is increasing in this younger age group. Equally, there are also reports of cases of anorexia with an onset in adulthood. As counsellors it is important for us to be aware of such data as the stereotype of the young teenage anorectic is deeply ingrained and may prevent us from picking up concerns about weight and size in those who do not fit the stereotype.

Nonetheless, the most typical anorectic is a girl or young woman. Concerns about body shape are not infrequent amongst adolescents. A recent study reveals that around 70 per cent of adolescent girls in a sample of school girls report having dieted to lose weight (Hill and Oliver 1992). Indeed, to be unconcerned by such matters does appear to be the exception. If you do not have any adolescent children, just think back to when you were an adolescent. It is likely that if you didn't go through a period when you suddenly became conscious of your body size and shape and may have wanted to change it, someone you knew experienced this.

But why should the most significant proportion of cases of anorexia emerge during adolescence? Many writers have highlighted the ways in which adolescence constitutes an important transition period in our lives – a time typically characterised by personal uncertainty and change as the individual begins to negotiate his or her independence. Adolescence involves a series of milestones that include establishing individual sexual, social and work lives and a positive sense of identity. The question of personal identity is central for the young person. Some children enter adolescence already possessing a sense of who they are and manage successfully to negotiate this developmental stage. This is achieved despite the confusion and change that adolescence brings. Other children, however, are less fortunate and reach adolescence with very little sense of who they are and may thus have to find themselves for the first time. For these, the changes associated with adolescence – changes in body shape and size, in relationships, in their awareness of their sexuality and in other people's expectations of them – may be experienced as particularly overwhelming and challenging, thereby shaking further the foundations of an already very precarious sense of self.

Clarifying one's sense of personal identity and position in the world are not easy tasks and it is perhaps not surprising to find that the adolescent turns to all available sources for help and guidance. Social norms and values are an important source of such guidance for they provide all of us with a ready-made reference point. The adolescent may choose to revolt against such norms and values, thus defining him/herself in contrast to them. Alternatively the adolescent may end up endorsing such values and identifying with them. It is not too difficult to imagine how a teenage girl in particular, growing up in a culture that values thinness and associates it with beauty, success, personal happiness and self-worth, should find herself identifying with such values and believing that by moulding her body according to prevailing cultural norms she has found a way to self-improvement. By doing so – as long as she does not become too severely emaciated – the young girl is indeed likely to receive praise for her weight loss. Such feedback may provide her with an important, *if not the only*, source of self-esteem and in many cases may also provide her with solutions to the numerous existential concerns that face us all. If the individual finds any kind of answer here to her existential dilemma, it is likely that a vicious cycle will be created which will trap the adolescent until she can find alternative ways to feel special and real.

Social class

Anorexia has long been thought of as a disorder of the affluent – the 'rich girl' syndrome. Bruch (1973), in one of her main works on the subject, reported that many of her patients' families came from a higher socio-economic background. Since then, others have confirmed Bruch's original findings. However, such a correlation needs to be interpreted with a degree of caution as it may simply reflect a bias of observation or in presentation to doctors. Those anorectics from a higher socio-economic background may simply have easier access to health care and may come from families that would encourage them to seek help. The statistics may therefore not provide an accurate reflection of what is actually happening but rather serve to reinforce an unfortunate stereotype which may in practice deflect attention and resources from those who need them most.

Cross-cultural factors

Until recently anorexia was regarded as an exclusively western problem and was associated with cultures obsessed with slender figures. It was generally held to be largely confined to white women. However, more recent evidence has challenged this prevailing assumption. Epidemiological research has shown that the incidence of anorexia in individuals of various ethnic origins is greater than it was originally believed to be. Anorexia has thus been well documented in Japan, in Blacks in the United States and in Britain, in Africa and in Asians in Malaysia. It has also been reported in adolescent Vietnamese refugees.

While it is likely that culturally determined attitudes to body shape may interact with psychological factors in the genesis of anorexia, what has been overooked until recently is the experience of those individuals who have emigrated to the West and have thus been exposed to a different, and often conflicting, set of socio-cultural norms and ideals. The confusion that is characteristic of adolescence, and which often centres around the individual's attempts to negotiate issues of autonomy, control and sexuality, may present particular difficulties for those adolescents growing up in a situation involving a juxtaposition of two very different cultures. Recent research by Mumford and her colleagues (1991) has shown that amongst a South Asian population of schoolgirls living in Britain, concerns around body shape and weight were associated with a more traditional cultural orientation and not, as might be expected, with greater 'westernisation'. Thus Di Nicola (1990) has proposed that anorexia may be viewed as a 'culture change syndrome' whose onset may be triggered under conditions of socio-cultural flux.

An estimation of the true rate of eating problems in non-white groups is impossible without a large epidemiological survey. Our own ethnocentric assumptions concerning the likelihood of a non-white individual presenting with an eating problem may be a source of bias. Because of the presumed uncommon occurrence of such problems in ethnic minorities it may be that we sometimes fail to recognise eating problems in such groups. At present the research alerts us to a vulnerability to anorexia in individuals of varied ethnic origins. More research is required in this very important area which challenges the stereotype of the white young woman who develops anorexia.

Men and anorexia

As we have seen, anorexia is not just confined to white middle-class adolescent girls. Rather women and children of all ages may develop it irrespective of their social class and ethnic origin. It is now also no longer recognised as an exclusively female problem. However, the occurrence of anorexia in males has been a sadly neglected area. Reports of anorexia in men are rarely found in the early medical literature and the current literature on this topic is still relatively scarce by comparison with that devoted to women.

The comparative rarity of male anorexia has been widely commented upon but now many researchers claim that up to 10 per cent of all cases are male and some go as far as to suggest that the condition is becoming more common in the male.

Many writers have drawn attention to the difficulty in diagnosing anorexia in the male, highlighting how, even when the diagnosis is made, it tends to be made later in men than in women. There are a number of factors that may account for such results and as counsellors it is essential that we should be aware of them.

Eating problems do occur less frequently in males and this fact alone may incline us to be less likely to think of it as a potential male problem. Our openness to the possibility of an eating problem in a male client may be further constrained by three factors.

Firstly, the language men tend to use to express their conflicts regarding their body shape and size may differ from that commonly used by women. For example, men rarely complain about how much they weigh or the size of the clothes they wear. Instead they are more likely to express a desire to lose 'flab' and to achieve what our culture considers to be a more classical male definition of muscle groups.

Secondly, the reasons men give for dieting may, at least superficially, sound more medically plausible. In one study some of the anorexic men reported having heard warnings directed towards a parent that they should lose weight in order to improve the symptoms of a medical condition such as heart disease. When accounting for their own weight loss the anorexic men tended to explain it in terms of health concerns rather than dissatisfaction with their own body shape (Andersen 1990). It is not clear why women who develop anorexia seldom begin to diet from fear of present or potential physical illness. This remains an interesting difference between male and female anorectics.

Thirdly, the methods men use to control their weight may attract less attention from others and may even be culturally valued activities. Many male anorectics use excessive exercise rather than self-imposed starvation to lose weight. The female anorectic's rejection of food is more likely to attract attention from those around her and to interfere more with her social life as so many of our social activities centre around food and eating. By contrast, the male anorectic's need to exercise fits in very well with an acceptable social activity – for instance, going to the gym with a friend. Thus the individual who self-starves will alert others more readily to the possibility of an eating problem in a way that the individual who compulsively exercises may not. In our fitness-conscious culture, the latter will not strike us as having a problem; rather we will probably admire his stamina and determination and praise him for his efforts. The greater likelihood of men using exercise rather than fasting as a means of controlling their weight is perhaps understandable in terms of sex-role expectations. It may then be that for many men problems comparable to anorexia are often masked beneath a preoccupation with exercise and sports.

Increasingly, researchers have devoted attention to the role of exercise in anorexia. Although such research is still relatively new, an Australian study found that exercise, and not dieting, was the main behaviour that precipitated severe weight loss in nine out of twenty-six cases of anorexia. The connection between exercise and anorexia is particularly striking among young athletes. Surveys of college athletes (both male and female) reveal that a large number admit to fasting as well as the use of vomiting and laxatives to control their weight. In males, the incidence of eating problems is higher amongst wrestlers, jockeys, runners and swimmers. Wrestlers in particular often undergo dramatic fluctuations in their intake of food if they are aiming for a particular weight class.

As in the case of female anorectics, a great deal of attention has been focused on the male anorectic's sexuality. Some have suggested that anorexic men tend to exhibit 'gender dysphoria' (i.e. unhappiness with their sexuality) and are more likely to be homosexual than their female counterparts. Statistics tend to support the suggestion that homosexual men are overrepresented in many samples of men with eating problems. While the proportion of male homosexuals in the American population cross-culturally is estimated to be 3–5 per cent, the incidence of those with eating problems has commonly been found to be twice as high or greater. However, such findings are based on clinical as opposed to community samples. The former may actually underrepresent heterosexual men, who may be more reluctant than homosexual men to seek help for what is stereotypically considered to be a 'female problem'. One study reported that 69 per cent of the male homosexual clients attending an eating problems unit were self-referred, compared to only 29 per cent of the heterosexual men, thus lending support to the notion of a bias in referrals (Herzog *et al.* 1990).

The literature on anorexia in men suggests that there are no significant differences between male and female cases of anorexia with regard to their clinical features, epidemiology and outcome (Scott 1986). The similarities include social class background and age of onset. Both men and women have been found to express 'overvalued ideas' with regard to weight and shape, and panic at the prospect of weight gain. Methods of weight control also show some similarity although women tend more to abuse laxatives whilst men are more likely to be involved in exercise.

While it may at first seem that many of the cultural explanations that have been invoked to account for the onset of anorexia in women could not apply to men, men may need help in coping with a different kind of cultural pressure and stereotype than that faced by women. While the societal pressures to be slim and svelte are exerted more strongly and consistently on women, frequently men also feel subtly or overtly under cultural pressure to achieve a classical male body shape. Homosexual men in particular may be at an increased risk of developing an eating problem because of cultural pressures within the homosexual community to be thin. Yager and colleagues (1988), for instance, found that male homosexual college students reported higher prevalences of bulimic behaviour and fears of weight gain than did a control group of heterosexual college men. Furthermore, men may be subjected to the demands of a 'macho' culture in which the display of emotion is taboo and where the valued activities and attitudes emphasise being strong and enjoying traditional male activities. Many men with anorexia are uncomfortable with this stereotyped role and are struggling to find a way to 'be' within such a world without feeling vulnerable to ridicule and rejection.

It appears then that a cultural pressure does exist for men also and this demands our acknowledgement. It cannot be dismissed as less important in the genesis of anorexia in men. When working with men who are anorexic we need to validate their experience of this pressure and, particularly as female counsellors, we must monitor our own feelings, as we may be tempted to undervalue such experiences in men.

WHY DO PEOPLE BECOME ANOREXIC?

Conceptual models of anorexia

The various factors that have been more consistently associated with anorexia lead us to speculate as to why some people become anorexic. Indeed questions of aetiology have long preoccupied clinicians and researchers. Currently, the explanations that are offered fit, by and large, into three models, namely the biomedical, socio-cultural and psychological models. These models are organised along different conceptual levels but they are not mutually exclusive. However, while they overlap to some degree, their main thrust and conceptualisations are distinct.

The biomedical model

The possible contribution of physical factors to the aetiology of anorexia was discussed right from the start. Since the 1970s a number of different endocrinological and neurological abnormalities have been postulated as possible causes of anorexia – for example, hormonal imbalance, dysfunctioning in the satiety centre of the hypothalamus and lesions in the limbic system of the brain. Overall, the thrust of biomedical investigations suggest that if anorexia is associated with an organic abnormality, the hypothalamus is the most plausible sight for the origin of the dysfunction.

Despite the fact that an organic cause of anorexia has not yet been established, proponents of a biomedical view have resorted to a wide variety of somatic remedies and drugs in its treatment. At various points in the twentieth century anorectics have been given thyroid extracts, insulin, corticosteroids, testosterone and lithium carbonate. Today, there is far less agreement about the use of medication in the treatment of anorexia.

Physicians' focus on the anorectic's body is understandable as anorexia is typically accompanied by characteristic physiological changes. The question, however, is whether the physical symptoms present in anorexia are primary or secondary in its aetiology.

The biomedical model presents some notable limitations in that it does not address important social characteristics of the anorexic population. It fails to account for the common observation that it is mainly young women and not young men who become anorexic and who are thus seemingly more susceptible to the particular biomedical disturbances that are highlighted by the proponents of this model of aetiology.

Some writers have argued that the observed gender skew may be more readily understandable if we turn our attention to some simple physiological, as opposed to biochemical, facts. From a physiological point of view, puberty is a time when weight gain for girls is primarily in fat rather than muscle, particularly in the breasts and hips. Puberty in boys however entails the growth of muscles and growing larger is frequently a source of pleasure and power for boys. Thus puberty, with its accompanying biological changes, takes girls further from our culture's pre-pubescent ideal body shape at a time when many girls come to believe that 'looks' are important. In other words, puberty, which may give the boy a sense of power, may be a time in the girl's life when she begins to feel powerless and dependent.

Even though, as we have seen, anorexia is no longer considered to be an exclusively western problem it remains true that the vast majority of cases are to be found in the developed countries of the West. Clearly, purely biomedical interpretations cannot account for these social facts. It is because of such considerations that the socio-cultural model of anorexia has continued to receive deserved attention.

The socio-cultural model

The socio-cultural explanation of anorexia is very popular. It suggests that in a society seduced by the angular, slimness has now become the most important attribute of female beauty. Anorexia is seen to be caused by the relentless emphasis on dieting – we idealise the image of the 'woman' the media constantly sells to us in its advertisements for diet products: 'beauty' without effort. Indeed, we are surrounded by images equating thinness and youth with glamour, fame and success. Women often compare themselves with such images and all too frequently feel themselves to be failures.

The pressure on women to diet and appear slim does indeed seem relentless. That such pressure may precipitate the development of anorexia seems to be supported by the finding that the condition is far more common in women who must rigorously control their size and shape, such as ballerinas and models. Such observations underscore the possible importance of our society's current value of thinness in women as a determinant in the increased prevalence of anorexia.

The most outspoken and influential proponents of this model of aetiology are feminists concerned with the full spectrum of eating problems. Within this conceptualisation, anorexia is seen as bearing witness to women's tortuous denial of need and dependency, as well as their persistent expressions of independence, so that women with anorexia appear to live out the contradictions of contemporary cultural dictates. Whilst manifestly the anorexic response is an attempt at a psychological solution, the point that many feminist writers are trying to make is that the solution that is sought, and the underlying psychology that makes such a response possible, are formed with reference to a particular set of social relationships which are inevitably bound up with the values inherent in our culture. As such, any treatment model that is generated to address the rise in anorexia needs to take into account the ways in which an individual's psychology absorbs and interprets cultural values.

The feminist interpretation of anorexia has much to commend it. Before the seminal work of Susie Orbach and the Womens' Therapy Centres in America and England, womens' dieting and weight concerns were, by and large, interpreted as masking a strictly individual psychological problem without taking into account the cultural influences on this behaviour. However, as Brumberg has pointed out, the explanatory power of the existing socio-cultural model is limited, as it rests on the implicit assumption that anorexia is a new phenomenon largely created by the pressures of contemporary western society. Whilst we have undoubtedly been witnessing an increase in anorexia since the 1960s, there is historical evidence to suggest that anorexia is not a 'new' problem resulting from the prevailing cultural imperative in the twentieth century for a thin female body (see Chapter 1).

It seems unlikely that the external forces highlighted by the socio-cultural model in themselves generate particular types of psychopathology; rather they give them shape and influence their frequency. Changing cultural environments also determine whether the anorectic is referred to as 'saint', 'hysteric', 'sick' or 'mad' and hence influence how we understand the anorectic's behaviour. However, it does not necessarily follow that if the ideal of thinness in our society changed to give way to a veneration for the curves of Rubens, the number of anorectics would diminish significantly. Under such hypothetical circumstances what might however be more likely is a decrease in the number of women attempting to lose a few pounds here and there.

Finally, as it stands, the socio-cultural model cannot account for the fact that so many individuals do not develop anorexia, even though they have been exposed to the same cultural environment. This is where individual psychology and family factors have a role to play.

Psychological models

Anorexia was recognised early as a psychosomatic syndrome. Under the influence of psychiatry and particularly of Freud's ideas in the twentieth century, many investigators in the field of psychosomatic medicine shifted from a concern for somatic manifestations to a concern for the psychological under-pinnings of these manifestations.

The psychological models of anorexia fall into three main groups, namely the psychodynamic, cognitive-behavioural and family systems models.

1 The psychodynamic model

The influence of the early psychodynamic thinking on the study of anorexia became the search for a specific psychodyna-mic of the 'illness'. The observation that anorexia did not gen-erally appear before puberty, that it was largely confined to girls, and associated with amenorrhoea, led many workers in this field to suggest that it was causally related to sexual development (see Chapter 1).

In the 1930s and 1940s, case reports of the psychoanalytical treatment of anorexic women emerged. Some authors referred to the repression of sexual phantasies, doubts about sexual potency, the denial of adulthood and the exclusion of adult problems and sexual needs. However, the attempt to explain anorexia with a single psychodynamic formulation was rend-ered impossible by the complexity of anorexia. Indeed, since the early psychoanalytic formulations the emphasis of psycho-dynamic writing has shifted. Ideas about the aetiology of anor-exia have dealt more in so-called 'borderline pathology'.

Hilde Bruch's writings have been particularly influential in the development of the psychoanalytic theory surrounding the aetiology of anorexia. Her thesis is that phantasies of oral impregnation, rather than being specific to anorexia, are fairly universal in childhood. When they appear in anorexia there-fore, they are viewed by Bruch as manifestations of immaturity and other developmental disturbances, but not the cause of them. The basic deficit in anorexia has its roots, according to Bruch, in the lack of recognition of child-initiated cues in the earliest mother–child relationship. The result is a passive, overcompliant child with little sense of self, identity and auton-omy, who finds the sexual impulses of adolescence a dangerous challenge and relieves her anxiety over losing control by the repression of sexual desire and starvation.

2   The cognitive-behavioural model

In the history of anorexia, the medical and psychodynamic models have been the two major governing approaches. In the past decade however, cognitive-behavioural approaches have been added to the conceptualisation and to the treatment of anorexia.

The main thrust of the cognitive-behavioural conceptualisation is that the central disturbance in anorexia is the individual's 'overvalued' ideas about shape and weight. It argues that most of the other features of anorexia (e.g. excessive exercising) are secondary to the individual's overvalued ideas.

The cognitive-behavioural counsellor views the beliefs and values of the anorectic as implicit rules which influence the way she evaluates and attributes meaning to her experience of herself and her world. Furthermore, the absolute nature of the beliefs and concensus held by the anorexic individual with regard to their shape and weight are said to reflect certain dysfunctional types of thinking. These include, amongst others, superstitious thinking and overgeneralisation. An example of the latter would be the belief that eating an extra slice of bread indicates the individual's total lack of self-control.

Such a model, whilst elucidating some of the factors that may contribute to the maintenance of the eating problem, does not however throw much light on why the individual may have developed such particular beliefs in the first place. Indeed, within the cognitive approach to treatment the 'why' of the behaviour is not considered to be very important.

3   The systemic model

Today, many investigators in anorexia are beginning to include in their formulations the interdependence of parts in a social context. The governing framework for their approach is the systems model. In the linear model, which encompasses all approaches that focus on the individual, the behaviour of an individual is seen as 'sparked off' by others or by the individual's beliefs or assumptions. In the systemic paradigm an individual's behaviour is simultaneously both caused and causative. Problems are thus understood as arising in the context of particular interactions between people.

Within the systemic model the interpersonal aspects of anorexia are emphasised, viewing the latter, amongst other things, as a phenomenon of regulation between two people, for instance between an 'overprotective' parent and a developing adolescent struggling to assert their autonomy. Anorexia is thus defined not only by the behaviour of the anorectic but also by the interrelationships of all family members. According to Minuchin, who has been an influential proponent of this particular model, certain kinds of environments encourage passive methods of defiance, for instance not eating, and make it difficult for members to assert their individuality (Minuchin *et al*. 1978). They describe the 'psychosomatic family' as controlling, perfectionistic and non-confrontational – adjectives which he equally applies to the anorectic. Minuchin has described what he calls the 'anorectic system' and identifies four factors which are typical of the anorexic family, namely enmeshment, overprotectiveness, rigidity and avoidance of conflict. Anorexia is thus understood as the only possible adaptation by a given individual to a given type of family functioning.

Where do we go from here?

This section has reviewed the main conceptual models that have been put forward to explain the genesis of anorexia. Throughout history the framework for the observation and thus the treatment of anorexia has expanded and changed. However, these changes of focus in the study of anorexia are not the result of any expansion in scientific knowledge. Rather they spring from different conceptualisations of the human being and his or her position in the world.

While it is possible that anorexia has a single discrete cause, it seems more likely that complex chains of events interact to precipitate its onset. Of all the models that have been reviewed, perhaps the socio-cultural model and the systemic model have the most to offer us in our attempts to comprehend the enigma of anorexia, as they both stress the circular interconnectedness between the individual, the family and culture. This is of particular relevance when we discuss a problem that pertains largely to women, as there has been a tendency to view womens' problems in particular as an expression of individual psychopathology, to be analysed and understood in the light of the individual's history.

In the light of such considerations both the systemic and socio-cultural models have a great deal to commend them, as they both try to incorporate in their formulations of clients' problems the context in which they live and within which their behaviour, feelings and thoughts arise and are challenged. Neither excludes the possibility that anorexia may well relate to early conflict and so to intrapsychic variables. More importantly, in both these models the locus of pathology is the individual in context as opposed to the biomedical, psychodynamic and cognitive-behavioural models, where the locus of pathology is solely the client. Indeed, linear thinkers treat the anorectic as a closed system responding only to her internalised context.

We may well benefit from taking both these models one step further and paying closer attention to the wider context within which all human behaviour takes place, that is 'existence' and what it means for human beings to 'be-in-the-world' and, even more to the point, what it means to 'be-in-a-body'. Rather than focusing solely on biology, individual psychopathology, the family or socio-cultural factors, anorexia may become more comprehensible if we begin to consider it as an individual's way of coping with life's essential paradoxes and anxieties. We will turn to such an understanding of anorexia in the next chapter.

DISCUSSION ISSUES

1 Which theoretical model, if any, do you think offers the most adequate explanation for the aetiology of anorexia?

2 Do you consider that cultural factors have the same impact on the genesis of anorexia in men as in women?

3 If cultural factors do play an important role in the aetiology of anorexia, what might be the implications of this for counselling someone who is anorexic?

4 To what extent do you think the gender of the counsellor might be important when working with an anorexic woman? With a man?

4

The Anorectic's Worldview

In the previous two chapters I have repeatedly used the label 'anorectic' to refer to the individual who self-starves. But who is the anorectic? What does she feel? What does she strive for? What is her project? To find answers to such questions and to understand the anorectic we have to go beyond the label and beyond that which is suggested by research.

THE NOTION OF A 'WORLDVIEW'

One way of conceptualising the commonalities between the experiences of those individuals who are anorexic is to think in terms of the anorectic's 'worldview'. This concept originates from the existential psychotherapeutic literature, the main concern of which has been to stress the importance of gaining insight into the client's experience of herself and her world. We all experience the world in different ways, even though the raw facts of our experiences may at times be very similar. However that which happens to us assumes a particular meaning and significance depending on our own beliefs, assumptions and values. These in turn constitute the very backbone of our own worldview. This notion is very useful in counselling as it serves to remind us that, as we all have a particular 'worldview', we must be careful not to assume too readily that we 'know' what, how or why our clients feel as they do. In this sense our own worldview will always impinge on our ability to listen to our clients.

The concept of a 'worldview' was originally put forward by the existential analyst Binswanger (1968). He postulated three modes of 'being-in-the-world' which characterise the existence of each one of us as 'beings-in-the-world', so that for each of us our worldview can be said to consist of three different dimensions – the *Umwelt*, the *Mitwelt* and the *Eigenwelt*.

The Umwelt refers literally to the 'world around'. It involves our relationship to the natural world; that is, the physical dimension of our existence. It is the world of laws and cycles, for instance, of being born and dying. The Mitwelt refers to the public world. It is the world of social relations but not of intimate relationships. The Eigenwelt is the private world. it refers to the relationship we all have with ourselves. However, it is not merely a subjective, inner experience. Rather, it is the basis on which we relate, and therefore includes our personal and intimate relationships. This dimension is crucially involved in our sense of reality. Finally van Deurzen-Smith (1988) has recently highlighted a fourth dimension, the *Uberwelt*. This refers to the ideal world, to the beliefs that we hold and that influence how we interpret the world.

We all live in all four dimensions simultaneously. However these four worlds are by no means four different worlds but rather four interrelated modes of 'being-in-the-world'. Binswanger pointed out that the reality of being-in-the-world for each individual can only be grasped if all modes are given equal importance and are addressed in their own right when trying to understand the client's difficulties. I shall now illustrate the insights that can be gained from such a perspective by way of an existential analysis of the anorectic's worldview.

THE ANORECTIC FORTRESS

The ways in which we relate to ourselves, our sense of who we are, will inevitably affect not only our experience of everyday social and intimate relationships but also how we experience the reality of what it means to be-in-the-world for human beings, that is, 'being-in-a-body'. This dimension is therefore a most important and fundamental dimension of a person's worldview. How is it reflected in the anorectic's experience of being-in-the-world?

Debbie was 16 when we first met. She was the second oldest of four children and lived with her mother and three brothers. The family moved from Scotland to London when Debbie was 13 as a result of her father's alcoholism, which often resulted in his physically abusing her mother. The move had been sudden and the family had subsequently spent a considerable length of time in a women's refuge. When they eventually found a home of their own it was very different from what Debbie had been used to in Scotland. Now the family lived in a cramped, run-down council flat in inner London where lack of privacy was a problem for all of them. Debbie remembered that she had been very upset by these events and that her life since had never seemed to be the same.

Mrs S., Debbie's mother, contacted me as she had begun to notice that Debbie was losing a lot of weight very rapidly. She had found remains of uneaten meals half flushed down the toilet and was finding it increasingly difficult to get Debbie to eat anything at all. Although Mrs S. had taken her daughter to the local GP, not only had Debbie refused to step onto the scales, but Mrs S. had felt that the doctor had not taken her concerns seriously and had only prescribed a tonic, assigning Debbie's erratic eating habits to 'exam pressure'.

Debbie was indeed due to sit her GCSE exams a few months later. She was an excellent student, hard-working and thoughtful, and was well liked by her teachers who described her as a 'perfectionist'. Mrs S. was also very proud of her daughter's academic achievements, particularly in the light of her three brothers' underachievement. Indeed, Mrs S. described her as the perfect daughter, who helped around the home, stayed in at night to keep her company, and who was in many ways a second mother to her brothers.

Mrs S. could not understand Debbie's sudden change. She had become 'secretive', 'a loner', 'moody', and she observed that Debbie spent most of her time either obsessively cleaning the house or counting calories and weighing her food.

Debbie was aware that she was 'in trouble'; however, she was not concerned by her loss of weight. What concerned her was that she could no longer concentrate on her school work and she remarked that she was losing interest in her peer group. She felt that she could no longer be part of it as her friends ridiculed her eating fads or engaged in activities that Debbie described as 'silly'. She felt very different from them and spoke of the need to believe in something beyond just 'having a good time' which she identified as being her peer group's reason for living.

She described how she had to make sure everything was clean around her. This was contributing to a lot of arguments with her brothers whom she described as 'messy' and having no aims in life (all her brothers were school truants and petty offenders). She spent all her pocket money on household cleaning items and said she enjoyed cleaning the house. She was very proud of this and she described how she could only relax if everything was spotless. However, she was even more proud of her self-control in relation to food. If she was able to adhere to her 500 calories per day diet, she said she felt happy and 'free as a bird'. If for any reason she could not keep to her carefully studied meal plans Debbie said she would start feeling very anxious and would then have to submit herself to even more rigorous dieting for the next few days.

Debbie expressed a great confusion about her life and what she wanted from it. She felt very hopeless when she thought about her future beyond her exams. Although she felt her mother had encouraged her studies, she had not felt supported in her attempts to explore a career or simply a life away from the family. Debbie herself found it difficult to envisage such a life because it conflicted so much with her family's values and aspirations.

Her closest 'companion' throughout this difficult period was her cat. She said that her cat was the only one who would let her 'be'. When Debbie thought of leaving home her plans had to take into account the welfare of her cat. Her ideal was to live in a small flat alone, and she derived much pleasure and comfort from her fantasies about how she would decorate the flat and particularly the fact that she would be able to decide whom to allow in. She thought she would no longer be disturbed by anyone and could get on with her diet without other people interfering in what seemed to have become her life project – to lose more and more weight.

Common sense alone would suggest that in order to be able to cope with what life 'throws' our way, we are greatly helped if we have a core sense of who we are, and that even though we may question everything else around us, we are not caught up in questioning our very identity and our sense of our existence. Moreover, van Deurzen-Smith argues that:

An intimate and secure relationship with oneself can only

be generated if some basic facts about life and death get faced.... Knowing that one is capable of standing alone even in the face of fate and disaster gives a sense of private reality which makes the world a less frightening and more rewarding place.

(1988: 96)

Debbie, however had no sense of being able to 'stand alone'. She depicted a childhood dominated by conformity. She described her upbringing as puritanical and felt from the start that 'someone out there had decided what I would be'. She recognised that in some ways she had felt very secure in this position as a lot of questions had seemingly been answered for her. Indeed, when Debbie began to explore her 'ideal world' in counselling she realised how she had never had values that she could call her own; that she had lived according to other people's standards of what was right or wrong. She had never really taken a stand for or against anything as she felt too insecure to be able to 'stand alone'.

Debbie's sudden uprooting to London and entry into adolescence had turned her world upside down. She gradually began to question who she really was. The person she had thought she knew and believed herself to be gradually became a stranger to her. She described feeling 'like a patchwork quilt' – lots of pieces had been sewn together but none belonged to her. Such a description of her 'self' reflected her deep conviction of not having an identity of her own, of experiencing her 'self' only as a reflection of other people's views of her while she remained empty – a 'nothing'.

Debbie realised she had never made any decisions about herself for herself and in counselling she began to understand her decision not to eat as being one of the few decisions she had ever made. She felt she had to hold on to this decision and be faithful to it every minute of her day. It was as though Debbie was defining her 'self' through her decision not to eat. The more others encouraged her to eat, the more Debbie became determined not to. Their pleading made Debbie even more resolute as it emphasised that this decision was all the more 'hers'.

Debbie enjoyed seeing her bones – the more they showed, the more she felt she was getting closer to who she really was.

Losing weight, thereby ridding herself of what she perceived to be layers of fat, and Debbie's obsession with cleanliness, seemed to be her attempts to cleanse herself of what she felt had been imposed on her by others. Indeed she often spoke of how she felt 'messy'. As Wyl Pennycook observed in relation to one of her clients, the individual is, through anorexia,

> rejecting her 'fate'; she is not living up to other people's expectations of who she should be. She is attempting to recreate life for herself on her terms. . . . She has to be psychically as well as physically pared to the bone – to deny her humanness in order, as she sees it, to become more human.
>
> (1987: 80)

Sheila McLeod (1981), who has written about her experience of anorexia, echoes such feelings when she recalls how she felt when she weighed under six stones: 'When I looked at myself in the mirror I saw someone beautiful; I saw myself . . . the clearer the outline of my skeleton became, the more I felt my true self to be emerging.' Later she adds: 'Without anorexia I should have been a "nothing".' Indeed, it was Bruch who identified that anorectics suffered from a deep fear of being a 'nothing'.

By becoming anorexic Debbie and Sheila McLeod in many ways did the only thing they felt they could do. They adopted the only strategy that was seemingly open to them in order to preserve a sense of identity, however precarious; to experience themselves as individual beings separate from their families and their expectations.

Their position in the world is strikingly similar to that described by Laing (1960) as the position of 'ontological insecurity'. Laing defines the ontologically secure individual as one who has a sense of her existence, of her reality and of her identity. This enables the individual to establish intimate relationships with others without feeling threatened. 'The individual', writes Laing,

> may experience his own being as real, alive, whole, as differentiated from the rest of the world in the ordinary circumstances so clearly that his identity and autonomy are never in question. . . . He thus has a firm core of ontological security.
>
> (1960: 41–2)

Laing also observed a counterpart to the above position, that of 'ontological insecurity'. The ontologically insecure individual finds it difficult to feel alive, real, differentiated. She feels constantly threatened and obliged to preserve her precarious sense of identity. Unlike the individual whose being is secure, in the primary experiential sense intended by Laing, where relationships with others are experienced as 'gratifying', the ontologically insecure person is preoccupied with preserving rather than gratifying himself. From such a position, what may to many appear to be day-to-day activities and inter-actions with others constitute a continual threat to the onto-logically insecure individual. If the individual cannot take her own sense of autonomy and identity for granted then she has to find ways of trying to be real and of preserving her identity.

Laing identified three forms of anxiety encountered by the ontologically insecure person: engulfment, implosion and pet-rification. Of all the three forms of anxiety the one which is experienced with particular poignancy by the anorectic is the fear of engulfment. This refers fundamentally to a fear of relationships as a result of the individual's uncertainty about the stability of her autonomy and identity. Relationships are threatening because merging with an other may involve a loss of self and autonomy, the very things that the anorectic is struggling to preserve.

Debbie found it difficult to be in crowds with others. She said it always felt as if she was suffocating. One other person could feel like a crowd to her. Indeed, Debbie had severed most of her links with other people, even those people whom she felt she had previously been close to. She described how she was unable to 'feel myself when I'm with others'. By this Debbie was not simply referring to the fact that she felt she had to put on an act in the presence of others but, more importantly, she literally felt she lost her 'self', that she almost ceased to exist when she was with other people. Her relation-ships within the family had become increasingly strained. She felt that they all criticised her behaviour and told her she was 'selfish' and 'mad'.

On one occasion she arrived at one of our sessions having just read an article on poisonous snakes. What had struck her most about this article was how it described the way 'snakes can sneak up to you, catching you unawares and kill you with just one bite'. This was a poignant metaphor for how Debbie experienced relationships with others. The world was a threatening place where Debbie felt she could constantly be attacked and she therefore sought refuge in her anorectic fortress.

As we saw in the previous chapter, there has been a belief that a conflict about sexuality has a central role to play in the aetiology of anorexia. In the light of our discussion here and the proposed description of the anorectic as ontologically insecure, it is perhaps not surprising that the anorectic presents us with so-called 'sexual problems'. Sex and sexuality are important, and often areas of potential conflict for many of us. For the anorectic, conflict in this area is likely to be exacerbated by the fear of engulfment: 'Engulfment is felt as a risk in being understood, in being loved, or even simply in being seen' (Laing 1960: 44). The precariousness of the anorectic's defensive stance and her fear of risking exposure render relationships of any nature difficult to establish and to sustain. Moreover the sexual fears and preoccupations of the anorectic are more likely to be the expression of their fear of psychological invasion.

However, whilst the anorectic may fear relationships with others, she also desperately wants to be loved. Laura's experiences highlight how the anorectic is caught in this dilemma. Laura was 32 years old when we first met. When she was 12 years old her parents separated and this resulted in her mother emigrating. Laura was left in London with her three younger brothers and her father. She remembers this time as being very confusing, not knowing what was going to happen from one minute to the next. She recalls that this is when she began to eat in a way that she now describes as being 'compulsive'.

Her father was a heavy drinker and regularly physically abused her. Laura said she lived in terror and believed that one day he would kill her. She never knew whether he would come home drunk and hit her, for instance for not having cleaned the house properly.

Although Laura was intelligent, she gradually dropped out of school as she could no longer face going in and pretending everything was fine. She felt she would have to pretend, as there was no one she could trust in or out of school. Her extended Muslim family were very critical of her. They constantly told her what to do, how to dress and so on. They did not allow for any deviation from their rules. Deviation led to punishment. Laura recalled that she no longer knew what to do and that 'everything felt like a real mess'.

This was Laura's life for three years. When she was 15 years old her father died due to the consequences of his alcohol problem and her mother returned to this country to live with her children. It was then that Laura began to diet excessively. She remembered thinking at the time that 'things are looking up for me'. The more weight she lost, the better she felt. The scales had become a powerful mediator between Laura's sense of herself and the world around her.

'Things', however, did not continue to 'look up' for Laura much longer. Although at first she was pleased her mother had returned, she felt she had very little in common with her and resented having to conform to what she felt her mother wanted her to be. She decided to leave home when she was 16 and got herself a job in a shop.

Laura was very frightened and more confused than she had ever been before. She no longer knew what could be believed in or whom she could trust. A few months following her move she was raped. She never reported the incident, fearing that no one would believe her. This experience left her feeling confused and further exacerbated her fear of other people. Following this incident Laura remembered feeling that she did not know who she was. She found it very difficult to establish close friendships and felt very isolated, albeit safer, as she felt she was not taking any risks. During this first year alone Laura started to binge and would alternate binging with very strict dieting. Often she would eat nothing and just 'drink myself into oblivion'.

Since that time Laura did not feel that much had changed in her life, although she had lived through a violent marriage and the birth and adoption of her child. She finally came to see me as she was increasingly concerned about, and felt restricted by, her eating problem. She continued to alternate binging and laxative abuse with very strict dieting. She could not bear to put on an extra pound and was always obsessively counting calories. She felt her life was immobilised by her eating practices – for example, she felt unable to apply for a job – and although she was not debilitated by severe emaciation, she felt handicapped by the way she lived her life 'in fear of calories'.

Laura eventually admitted in counselling to longing for a relationship with another person but being very frightened to engage in one. She had never been able to forget her negative experience with her father who had physically abused her. She had been terrified of him but had also felt very dependent on him. What she perceived to be her dependency had cost her a lot – a battered body and a battered sense of self. This experience was then repeated with her husband and Laura concluded from both these experiences that 'others can give you nothing, they only beat things out of you'. In her marriage Laura had felt that she had given everything to her husband and that she had been like a 'shadow' to him.

Laura's fear of intimacy seemed to result partly from her fear of dependency. Her perceived overwhelming dependency, which had caused her to feel out of control in her relationships with others, led her to seek autonomy in the only area of her life where she felt she could experience some: in relation to her body. This is how Laura described her experience:

> I can't explain how happy and relieved I can feel when I know I have lost some weight. As I stand on the scales and see that number I forget all my worries. I feel relieved. I feel this is me and the more weight I can lose the more I feel I have done good. I can be proud of myself no matter what others out there think about me and I feel I don't need them.

It was only when Laura could step on the scales, religiously, at the same time each morning, that she was able to recapture her euphoria and, more importantly, what she felt was a sense of herself.

Laura's quest for physical perfection was a manifestation of her search for control in a situation where she had long felt powerless. For her, as for many anorectics, thinness was the vehicle rather than the goal of her pursuit. The goal was to gain a sense of being *someone* and to feel able to control at least one aspect of her life. But her position was potentially so unstable that she could not allow any intrusion from others into her adjustment. The precariousness of this position is such that it is possible to understand how intimate relationships may be experienced by the anorectic as threatening even though on one level they may be longed for. However, the polarity for the ontologically insecure individual is between complete isolation or complete merging of identity rather than between separateness and relatedness.

The answer to the conflict between autonomy and dependency which underlies the anorectic's struggle is to be found in an integration of these two polarities. This is likely to be difficult for the anorectic and she will often struggle with her ambivalent feelings. Laura, for example, was unable to manage the ambivalence and her initial solution was to deny her dependency by retreating into the anorectic fortress. Her fear was that if she admitted to her need for others then she would be lost and her deep conviction of being a 'nothing' would be confirmed. The anorectic's difficulty in managing her ambivalent feelings in relation to her own needs frequently sets in motion the operation of splitting mechanisms. This may include the denial of her own needs, symbolically expressed in her denial of hunger, and the projection of her own needs onto others, who may then be perceived as weak, messy or greedy.

BEING-IN-A-BODY

Being-in-the-world for human beings entails at the most basic level 'being-in-a-body'. This fact can be experienced in varying ways, ranging from the body being taken for granted to the body being experienced as an alien entity which has to be controlled and subjected to the most strenuous exercise and/ or intransigent eating practices as evidenced in anorexia.

Anorexia bears witness to a striking dissociation between the body one is and the body one has. It is in this split that the anorectic's struggle is located. Laura never experienced a sense of being at one with her body. The body was merely an impingement, an unwelcome intruder into an existence that Laura felt had been slowly 'eaten away by others'. The body was a nuisance to Laura – eating, going to the toilet, menstruation, were all unwelcome reminders of 'this body' that she so much wanted to disown. Although by the time I met her Laura menstruated regularly there was a time when menstruation had ceased. This is a state she at times suggested she would like to return to as periods were experienced by Laura as a sore reminder of reality. Such feelings are echoed by Karen

45

Margolis (1988) whose experience of anorexia is chronicled in her book *To Eat or Not To Eat*. For her the loss of her periods:

> was a relief because I could forget an inconvenient bodily function: it took me further towards the goal I was developing. There is nothing so potent a reminder of reality than the blood stains on your panties. I wanted to forget reality.

Such feelings about the body are very frequent amongst anorectics. 'I want to be thin because I don't like flesh', writes Sheila McLeod. Flesh is experienced as dirt and pollution. It is a foreign entity that needs to be kept at bay and what better way than by reducing its volume, by paring oneself to the bone. We will see later how such negative associations, rather than being the product of a 'sick' mind, are in fact the result of societal conceptions of the female body.

Any violation of their self-imposed harsh rules about what may or may not be eaten causes anorectics to feel guilty for having given in to the gross and vulgar demands of the body, and they condemn themselves to even more strict dieting. Indeed, as Karen Margolis observes, for the anorectic 'there is something indecent about eating ... the opening and closing of mouths. ... Admission of appetite and of bodily needs.' But the anorectic, through her self-imposed starvation does not have to be part of the crowd of people 'masticating like animals'. Moreover, anorexia offers its sufferers admission into an illusory world where they can feel 'superior to everyone else, to the material world that needed to eat and sleep and keep both feet on the ground'. Equating the feeling she obtained through fasting to that reached by mystics, Margolis felt that through starvation, she had found a way to retreat inside herself and so 'shut out the ugliness of human existence'.

If the self-starvation proceeds the anorectic begins to discover, often for the first time, what it feels like to be powerful, special, different. As Debbie pursued her strict diet she began to feel different and superior to her peer group. She even admitted that she hoped none of her friends at school would start dieting in this way, otherwise she would no longer 'stand out'. As the anorexia tightened its grip, Debbie started to feel she had very little in common with her peer group and their 'petty' concerns. She was not interested in who was going out with whom or any such things. She experienced herself as being above such concerns.

The material world had to be grappled with and controlled and the more Debbie succeeded at this, as she saw it, through her self-starvation, the better she felt about herself. The body was her only weapon in a bid for autonomy. It was the only thing that Debbie felt she owned but, without realising, she was doing her best to disown it.

The rejection of the flesh that was noted earlier has, at times, been interpreted as a rejection of life. Indeed Boss (1955) put forward the notion of suicide in 'refractive doses' – that is, a slow drawn-out form of suicide – when referring to patients who refused to live as 'beings-in-a-body'. Although it is easy to understand how one might arrive at such an interpretation of anorexia, as it can on the surface appear to be very self-destructive, anorectics are telling a very different story.

Sheila McLeod explains how anorexia in fact denies the reality of death: 'Death ... is a biological fact but anorexia entails a denial of biology and in particular the notion of biology as destiny. ... When I was anorexic I postponed the idea of myself-as-mortal.' Such observations are echoed by Karen Margolis: 'Suspended between menarche and menopause I was able during my hunger strike to transcend age.' She goes on to stress that when she spoke of death or suicide, 'I meant the end of the flesh, never imagining that I would lose my mind. ... I desired a reincarnation into another form, not a rebirth in the uncomfortable world of flesh.' Indeed, it is the anorectic's determination to be a self-defined, autonomous, individual that leads her to reject the option of suicide and to choose the far more difficult life of self-starvation – not in order to die, but in order to go on living. As Palazzoli points out:

> This type of acarnality is not a death wish. ... It is, essentially, an unrealistic tension and a rejection of existence qua living and dying in one's body ... it is a rejection of death as a biological fact and with it a rejection of ageing, corpulence and existential decay.
>
> (1974: 81)

Thus, if we are prepared to enter the anorectic's world we will begin to understand that anorexia, rather than expressing a death wish, expresses a wish to live as a self-respecting individual and paradoxically offers the anorectic, as in the case of McLeod and Margolis, a means of coping with death anxiety. Indeed, anorexia provided both these women with a feeling of specialness and omnipotence reminiscent of childhood when such issues are not, by and large, at the forefront of our minds. The feelings of specialness enabled both Margolis and McLeod to feel above such mortal concerns. Thus McLeod writes: 'Anorexia provided me with the illusion that I was in control of my body and of the biological processes which others around me were powerless to influence. In short I became convinced of my own omnipotence.' Recalling when the school nurse warned her that she would die if she did not eat, she writes: 'I didn't believe her, my own sense of superiority had extended itself to include a conviction in my own immortality.' The need to sustain the feelings of specialness and of difference is so strong that Margolis felt that 'to admit I enjoyed anything would mar my perfection, would consign me back among the mortals with their feet on the ground'.

Such personal accounts suggest that anorexia provides a paradoxical solution to, amongst other things, death anxiety. The defence employed by the anorectic in this case is the 'belief in personal specialness' (Yalom 1980). This belief allows the individual to deal with existential anxieties. For instance, the anorectic's belief that she is special and different – a belief that is reinforced by the 'benefits' derived from her self-starvation – enables her to live as though she is exempt from natural laws and thus helps her to quench death anxiety. For facing the inevitability of our death and accepting that the universe does not acknowledge one's specialness requires a secure sense of self. However, as I have suggested, the anorectic's starting point is the position of ontological insecurity.

As the emerging anorectic regresses into her more restricted and seemingly simpler existence, she experiences a sense of renewed control over her destiny. As McLeod writes: 'Unless I impose some form and order on life I shall lose control, chaos will ensue and life will become meaningless.' By virtue of the experience of being in control that anorexia affords its sufferers, the experienced chaos and the actual or potential conflict decrease. So long as she can hold on to her new position she is secure. Meanwhile, her existential anxieties have been alleviated and replaced by a total fear-driven concern about maintaining her low body weight. What characterises the anorectic's relationship to the natural world is a denial that she is part of it, for much of what is natural, such as death, is ultimately not within our sphere of control. Debbie's very strained relationship with the natural world extended itself, for instance, to finding it difficult to accept changes in the weather. She liked the sun and on several occasions when a sunny weather forecast had proved inaccurate she would express a great deal of anger towards the forecasters for having 'got it wrong again'. What underpinned her anger was the difficulty in coping with the unpredictability of the natural world, for its very unpredictability was a sore reminder that she was, like all of us, at the mercy of natural laws and cycles.

However, for the anorectic, as we have seen, to be in control is all-important. By denying her being as one in any way related to her body the anorectic finds a way of relieving a great deal of anxiety, and not only death anxiety as suggested earlier. For this form of denial also enables the anorectic to sidestep the issues of sexuality and intimacy that are frightening for her as they both threaten her with the possibility of engulfment. By creating the illusion that she is becoming more and more detached from her body and its functions, the anorectic can start to feel in control, as she is convicing herself that the body has nothing to do with her.

Finally, not only is the anorectic unable to tolerate the unpredictability and at times 'unfairness' of the natural world, she is equally unable to feel part of what is beautiful and alive in it. McLeod poignantly illustrates this point when she recounts the experience of listening to William Blake's poem:

> Oh sunflower, weary of time
> Who countest the steps of the sun
> Seeking after that sweet golden clime
> Where the travellers journey is done

As McLeod recalls:

> These words filled me with nausea, pain and anger ... they seemed to express my own weariness, my own longing to be something or somewhere other than I was. They also brought home to me the fact that although I, like the sunflower and

all other organic things, was living out a natural cycle, I had somehow shut myself out, cut myself off from nature, of which I was inevitably, inescapably a part.

THE BODY-IN-SOCIETY

In exploring the anorectic's relationship to her body and the implications of what it means for her to be-in-a-body, I addressed the physical dimension of existence. However, being-in-a-body is not only a biological fact, it is also a social fact. Palazzoli remarks that 'the body is our meeting place with others and its rejection is at one and the same time a rejection of sociability, human solidarity and responsibility' (1974: 152). Thus the body represents both concretely and symbolically the meeting place with others and is therefore involved in our experiences and interactions in the public world. Thus the body has to be grasped in its concrete existence socially and historically before we can begin to understand how it has the potential to assume such negative existential implications for the anorectic.

The public world of women, as it were, has long been dominated and shaped by the belief that 'anatomy is destiny'. The female body has been associated with what is weak, impure and corrupt; the site of discharges and bleedings. All these are negative associations and such notions feed into the anorectic's experience of her body as something she needs to disown because it seems to be so much out of her control and therefore cannot be trusted. Thus, besides the natural implications of what it means to be-in-a-body – which apply equally to men and women – important messages are conveyed through the social construction of the female body. These messages can affect the way in which biological changes are experienced by women. It is during adolescence – the time when a large number of anorectics emerge – that the stage is set for women to be defined through their bodies.

Simone de Beauvoir eloquently described how uncertain the feminine hold on the world is. She suggested that women do not experience encounters with others as occasions for taking but for being taken. For de Beauvoir this was because the woman has a body that allows her to be taken. She notes that at puberty:

The young girl feels that her body is getting away from her, it is no longer the straightforward expression of her individuality; it becomes foreign to her; and at the same time she becomes for others a thing: on the streets men follow her with their eyes and comment on her anatomy. She would like to be invisible; it frightens her to become flesh and show her flesh.

(1949: 333)

This is the social dimension of what it means to be-in-a-body, particularly for women, and it is this dimension, as we saw in the last chapter, that the socio-cultural model of anorexia has largely focused on, highlighting its implications in the increased incidence of anorexia. However, what is of relevance to our discussion is not whether socio-cultural factors are implicated in the aetiology of anorexia, but rather how the social dimension of being-in-a-body is reflected in the anorectic's experience of the public world.

Laura was very conscious of her body. This is not surprising as her body had been abused by her father, her husband and when she was raped. It was therefore experienced by Laura, in a very real sense, as a site for invasion and attack by others. Indeed, she often felt it was being 'invaded by others' looks'. 'Others' referred largely to men, although when Laura was feeling particularly insecure women's looks would also be experienced in a similar way. When she went out she felt exposed to lewd looks and such was her discomfort and fear on these occasions that she preferred to spend most of her time indoors. On those rare occasions when she left her bed-sit (for example to come to sessions or to collect her social security money), she was often overwhelmed by debilitating panic attacks. Laura described herself as 'paranoid' in the streets. She never felt safe: 'I walk and I'm constantly aware that I could be attacked at any time from any side.' Laura was not referring to merely physical attack. She felt she could be robbed of her 'self'. Staying in her bed-sit, however lonely she might be, often felt safest.

Laura felt powerless and invalidated by her public world interactions to the point where those interactions became fewer and fewer. She said she could not 'afford' to be with others when she was in pain. She thought 'others' were able

51

to see right through her and if they saw her pain they would take advantage of her. Such fears were reflected in the pattern of her attendance at the Centre where we met. For a long period of time she would only attend the Centre when she was feeling relatively strong. If she was in pain she would not attend and would not even risk going out to telephone to let me know that she would not be coming.

Debbie's experience of the public world was very similar to Laura's. Debbie was a very attractive young woman and as she put it, 'I was always very popular with the boys'. Although she remembered having enjoyed this initially, she was left feeling that the only reason she was popular was because she was attractive and not because 'I had any worth as a human being'. This set up a fundamental conflict between the physical and the moral. As the signs of her femininity became outward and visible, and Debbie could no longer avoid attracting, as it were, she experienced this at a very deep level as the surrender of her identity to that conferred on her by the gaze of the 'other'. She gradually stopped mixing with her peer group and generally going out. Through her anorexia Debbie appeared to be struggling to find a new basis from which she could be her own woman and not a woman for 'others'; to live by norms of her own and not those prescribed by her family, her school and society as a whole. Ultimately she was trying to be a person in her own right and abandon the 'patchwork quilt' image of her 'self'.

Both Laura's and Debbie's relationship with the public world was characterised by a gradual withdrawal from this dimension of their lives as they both experienced relationships with others as potentially dangerous. They both experienced their bodies as a potential site for connection with others but they also felt that this was a very vulnerable 'site' – one that could easily be invaded and taken over by others. From their position of ontological insecurity they could not conceive of any middle way as for them to be seen was to be potentially 'engulfed'.

What appears to underlie such an experience of relationships with others, both intimate and public, is a pervasive sense of inffectiveness and powerlessness. Indeed, Palazzoli observed that anorectics tended to have led a compliant lifestyle that interfered with the child's development of a sense of self-awareness and of self-identification, thereby producing a very severe atrophy of the feeling that it is possible to influence people or things in a significant way. Bruch (1979) also identified a paralysing sense of ineffectiveness and the conviction of being helpless to change anything, as being one of the main pre-illness features of anorexia. The anorexic women Bruch worked with had, according to her, all led compliant lifestyles, trying to live up to other people's expectations, always fearing they were not good enough in comparison with others and felt themselves therefore to be disappointing failures. This led Bruch to conclude that an imbalance of power had existed throughout the child's life and to view the child's agreeable compliance as an attempt to conceal the fact that she had been deprived by her parents of the right to live her life.

Drawing from Sartre's description of the paradox of human relationships consisting of our desire to dominate others while being exposed to others' attempts to dominate us in turn, van Deurzen-Smith highlights how the power conflict can be solved in three ways:

> One can attempt to gain mastery over others. One can submit to others or devote oneself to them and make oneself indispensable to them in this way. One can finally withdraw from contact with others entirely and thus avoid the conflict, at least momentarily.
>
> (1988: 78)

The anorectic seems to be opting for the last choice, that of withdrawing. As she feels powerless and ineffective she tries to avoid the conflict inherent in human relationships by withdrawing from the world of public and intimate relationships. Margolis describes how she ended up avoiding social contact with strangers because 'I could not rely on their accepting me as I wanted to be seen and taking on their required roles'. She identified other people as being her greatest 'fear'.

The anorectic's social withdrawal has led some investigators to state that the anorexic condition reflects a retreat from growth – a state of 'giving up'. Although the observation that the anorectic withdraws from social interaction is accurate, we need to be cautious as to whether we interpret this as a state of 'giving up'.

Debbie's, Laura's and Karen Margolis' withdrawal from social interaction was not an indication that they had 'given up' or stopped their fight to be autonomous human beings. The social withdrawal – which is facilitated by not eating, as relationships often involve eating and drinking – is a desperate attempt to preserve what is experienced to be a very precarious sense of self, so that life may indeed continue. As was suggested earlier, anorexia is not a death wish. Rather, it is an imagined solution for the individual, a way of 'being-in-the-world'.

Finally, when we encounter the anorectic in the public world we encounter an individual who feels powerless to influence others and for whom others represent a threat. Her experience is embedded in a social and cultural environment which has added to her confusion about her body beyond the existential implications of what it means to be-in-a-body for all of us alike.

BEYOND THE 'GOLDEN CAGE'

This chapter has introduced the notion of 'worldview' and used this to trace some of the commonalities that appear to characterise the anorectic's experiences. The anorectic's worldview appears to be dominated by one polarity – that of control, versus chaos. The body and its functions have to be controlled, as well as relationships with others. If she feels that she cannot exert this type of control then she fears chaos will ensue and that she will be swallowed up in a sea of confusion or by an 'other' – and then there would be nothing left of her 'self'. Such is the precariousness of the anorectic's defensive stance that she cannot allow herself a moment's relief from what appears to have become her life project – self-starvation.

Although I have suggested that the anorectic's 'being-in-the-world' is overpowered and ruled by the category of 'control versus chaos', this is not to deny that she may be struggling to hold on to her power of self-determination. Her struggle, as we have seen, takes on the form of renouncing certain of her potentialities in order to ward off the threat of dissolution of her world and hence of the dissolution of the 'self'. But since it is just this renouncing of potentials of existence that represents the beginning of the dissolution of the self, all such efforts lead to their own negation and the anorectic finds herself caught in a bind. As Palazzoli remarked in relation to one of her patients:

> ... and so the young anorexic was caught in a cruel trap. She refused to eat in order to preserve her personal identity, but in order to preserve her life she simply had to eat and this she experienced as an act of self betrayal.
>
> (1974: 65)

'To become anorexic', Edwards writes, 'is to create and inhabit a nightmarish world within which basic human needs cannot and will not be met – an ascetic prison with ever-narrowing boundaries' (1987: 61). Indeed, this is what Bruch aptly referred to as the 'Golden Cage'. In the next chapter I will address what we, as counsellors, may benefit from paying attention to if we want to help the anorectic take the risk to come out of her 'cage' and fulfil her existential possibilities.

DISCUSSION ISSUES

1 'The anorectic speaks through her body and her body finds a solution to psychic pain.' Can you think of any personal experiences when you bypassed language and expressed what you were feeling through your body (e.g. by becoming ill)? What (dis)advantages did this means of communication hold for you?

2 What is your experience of 'being-in-a-body'?

3 Would you agree with the hypothesis suggested in this chapter that anorexia – even of a life-threatening nature – might paradoxically be used in the service of psychic survival?

5

On the Question of 'Cure'

Counselling the anorectic

In the last chapter I sketched out what I referred to as the 'anorectic worldview', emphasising in particular how the anorectic finds a solution to some of her anxieties by exerting relentless control over her body and by withdrawing from relationships with others, as these threaten her with the possibility of engulfment. Faced with an individual in such a predicament, what can a counsellor offer?

This question has received as many answers as it has stimulated theories to account for the aetiology of anorexia (see Chapter 3). All the theories and their assumptions about aetiology have implications for how we approach our work with an anorexic client. The theories help us to define our role in relation to our clients. For instance, adding flesh to the anorectic's emaciated body was the nineteenth-century physician's challenge. Then, medical success was measured in terms of weight gain. Relatively little attention was devoted to why the individual should be starving herself and even less to attempting to gain an insight into the world of the anorectic. Once the doctor had determined that the individual had no organic reason to refuse food, the medical course of action was simple: she had to be fed by whatever means were available. When it was deemed by the doctors that a reasonable weight had been reached, the 'patient' was declared cured without further investigation of why she had stopped eating in the first place. The emphasis on weight gain that dominated the nineteenth-century treatment of anorexia persists to this day and it underscores a number of current treatment approaches.

Whilst there are important differences between the treatment approaches that stem from the various theoretical orientations, they all have one thing in common, namely that they all meet the difficulty of actually helping the anorectic to change her behaviour. 'Therapeutic failures' and reports of deaths are by no means uncommon in the literature.

COMMON TREATMENTS FOR ANOREXIA

When you first meet an anorexic client it is possible that they will have already seen other practitioners for consultation as well as having received particular types of treatment. Most commonly, if GPs are concerned about one of their patients losing weight and experiencing problems around eating, they will tend to make a referral to a clinical psychology department. In some extreme cases a referral may be made directly to a consultant psychiatrist and a request for hospital admission may be made. The admission to hospital may be carried out against the client's will under the aegis of the Mental Health Act 1983 which allows compulsory admission to hospital in cases where the individual's behaviour may be life-threatening.

If referred to a clinical psychologist the individual may be offered a number of options. They may be offered individual psychotherapy. However, psychotherapy on the National Health Service is a scarce resource and it is thus more likely that your client will have received other forms of treatment. Many psychologists now offer cognitive-behaviour therapy for a range of problems, including eating problems. Cognitive-behavioural interventions aim at challenging the dysfunctional assumptions and negative thoughts believed to be at the root of the eating problem. They aim to help clients to articulate and examine the thoughts and attitudes which motivate them to self-starve, thus precluding change in this behaviour. This is what is referred to as 'cognitive restructuring'. To this end, the psychologist may suggest to the client that they keep a record of their thoughts concerned with shape and weight. This may be done by keeping a daily diary which the client is then invited to share within the session. The aim is to elicit 'problematic thoughts' so that the client may begin to explore their reactions to the occurrence of such thoughts and so identify triggers for them.

Some psychology departments may offer group treatment.

The therapeutic orientation and structure of the groups will vary but it is most likely that the groups will be structured and open to individuals who are anorexic and bulimic.

If your client is an adolescent they may well have had previous experience of family therapy as this is frequently the treatment of choice with younger clients. It is probably true that the younger anorexic clients are more amenable to family treatment. If one believes that it is important to intervene in the anorectic's context, the most immediate contextual field of the child is the family and, at a young age, this is likely to be accessible. In this respect one can see that it makes sense to treat the child as being very much part of a family.

However, the older the anorectic, the more resistant she is likely to be to such an approach. The findings of a study by Russell *et al*. (1987) are of particular relevance. They ran a study comparing family therapy with individual supportive psychotherapy and found that the former was more effective with individuals whose anorexia was not chronic and had begun before the age of 18. However a more tentative, but interesting, finding was the greater value of individual supportive psychotherapy with older anorectics.

Finally, you may be referred a client who has had experience of in-patient treatment aimed at weight restoration. When weight restoration takes place in a hospital, the individual is gradually introduced to the consumption of regular meals and by the end of two weeks these are expected to be of normal quantity and composition, consisting of around 2500 kcal a day. The latter amount does vary and may exceed 2500 kcal. If such a programme fails more strict 'operant' behavioural programmes may be introduced whereby 'privileges', such as watching TV or seeing visitors, are withdrawn until some weight has been gained.

If we pause to consider the anorectic's position it is not very difficult to imagine how she might feel at the prospect of being hospitalised. 'The hospital', writes McLeod, 'must seem like a prison where she is being punished for seeking autonomy by being deprived of what little autonomy she has managed to find' (1981: 112). It is therefore not surprising to find that even though the anorectic usually puts on weight whilst she is receiving in-patient treatment of the kind discussed here, she often loses the weight when she leaves the hospital.

Behavioural treatment programmes are indeed paradoxical. The individual who has managed to get by with her life of starvation is in hospital deprived of the very act that enabled her to preserve a sense of 'self'. As Bruch remarked with regard to such interventions, their very efficiency 'increases the inner turmoil and sense of helplessness in these youngsters who feel tricked into relinquishing the last vestiges of control over their bodies and their lives' (1979: 108). The use of the word 'tricked' by Bruch seems most appropriate as it reflects the experiences shared with me by many anorectics who have undergone such treatment.

Clients frequently bring their previous experiences of treatment to bear on their relationship with their counsellor. Such experiences may have been painful and may colour the client's expectations of what you, as their counsellor, are going to do. For this reason it is important to be as frank and as open as possible with the anorectic. This clearly requires the counsellor's willingness to clarify their therapeutic aims and hidden agendas. This will be particularly important if one is working for an institution, such as a hospital, where the aims of the system influence the therapeutic work and where the primary concern may be that the client puts on weight.

It is important to be sensitive to the client's anxieties about what you may be offering them. The exploration of the client's fantasies about what you might do will also be important. Very often the issues concern who will have ultimate control over the client's life. This can trigger extreme anxiety on the part of the client and it raises ethical dilemmas for the counsellor, to which we shall return later in Chapter 6.

Outcome of anorexia

The outcome of treatment is not easy to assess. Whilst, in the short term, weight restoration can be achieved by following the regimes that are imposed upon individuals as in-patients, more permanent changes have proved to be somewhat elusive.

The reported recovery rates for anorexia vary considerably from study to study, depending on differing diagnostic criteria, patient selection, length and type of follow-up, and measures of outcome. The recovery rate is thus reported as lying anywhere between 23 per cent and 86 per cent. More generally, while

bearing in mind that comparisons between studies are difficult, the suggestion is that about 75 per cent of anorectics are
better at follow-up than at initital presentation, at least in
terms of body weight. However, outcome according to menstrual function is less satisfactory, and according to psychiatric
status even less so. Social adjustment is also impoverished in a
large proportion of cases. Poor outcome is frequently associated
with the following:

1 longer duration of the eating problem;

2 older age of onset and at presentation;

3 low weight during the illness and at presentation;

4 presence of symptoms such as vomiting;

5 poor parental relationships.

Is one approach more effective than any other?

Studies comparing the effectiveness of different approaches
are infrequent in the literature. Most of the published studies
tend to focus on in-patient management programmes and
consequently there is little that can be extrapolated from such
studies that could be of use to counsellors. There is a need for
more reports from individuals who are practising either in out-
patient units or privately whose approaches with this particular client group appear to be 'successful'.

To those brave enough to venture into the research literature
on treatment outcome I would offer a word of caution: pay
particular attention to the outcome measures that the
researchers have employed. Although the concept of 'cure' is
at best an elusive one, because of its somatic components, the
anorectic can be said to have been cured when her weight
has been restored to her AEBW or, if we are interested in
psychosocial and psychosexual measures, when functioning
in these areas shows improvement to a normal level. Therefore, when assessing the claims of a particular therapeutic
intervention, we need to ask ourselves what it is exactly that
this method claims to be able to 'cure'.

IS COUNSELLING ANORECTICS ANY DIFFERENT TO
COUNSELLING OTHER CLIENT GROUPS?

There is a school of thought within counselling that suggests that different client groups may not only require us to adapt our methods of working but also require some specific knowledge, if not first-hand experience, of the presenting problem. This has led to a proliferation of specialist counselling services, including specialist services for those presenting with an eating problem.

It is certainly true that in the case of anorexia it is important to have some reference points. For instance, it is essential to be aware of the physical complications that may arise, as well as the manifestation of such problems in men and different ethnic groups. In this sense it can be argued that counsellors working with anoretics require specialist knowledge. However, I am far more sceptical of suggestions that counsellors may require specialist training to develop particular techniques for approaching the presenting problem, even though different schools of thought have all made their bid at different points in time for providing 'the' answer to anorexia.

Whilst it is of interest and important to familiarise oneself with the assumptions and techniques of the different theoretical orientations, it is not the aim of this book to offer such an overview. However suggestions for further reading can be found at the end of the book.

Counselling anorectics is not essentially different to counselling any other type of client. It may well *feel* different however, because of the nature of the problem. Its defiance in the face of help, its potentially life-threatening nature and the cultural values often reflected in the anorexic struggle may present a particular challenge to the counsellor. For such reasons alone counselling anorectics may lead us to feel that we need to develop some 'special' techniques. At times our search from workshop to bookshop for 'the' answer belies our own anxieties. It also perhaps alerts us to an implicit assumption that counselling is more about the acquisition of skills and techniques rather than the outcome of thoughtful introspection and a willingness to be challenged and to relinquish our preconceptions about how or why the anorectic feels as she does.

Notwithstanding such cautionary comments about 'specialisms', there are a number of guidelines for 'good' practice, beyond any particular theoretical allegiances, that should underpin any attempt to offer counselling to the anorexic individual. There are also a number of issues that pertain to working with someone who is anorexic which deserve careful consideration by those wishing to undertake counselling work with such clients. It is to these that we shall now turn.

OBSTACLES TO COUNSELLING

Those individuals who become anorexic have retained the reputation of being difficult to 'treat' or to 'help'. Indeed, a great deal of emphasis has been placed on the 'chronicity' of anorexia. Many professionals find working with anorectics difficult and wearing. The endless devices she uses to ensure that she does not put on any weight have earned the anorectic the reputation of being 'manipulative', 'devious' and 'deceitful'. The anorectic's apparent stubbornness in the face of impending death and pleas by all around to eat can be experienced as frustrating as it seemingly blocks all attempts to help her. Her rejection of our attempts to help her can be very wounding and may arouse in us retaliatory feelings. Anorexia therefore appears to pose a great challenge to those who attempt to 'cure' it – not least the question of whether the anorectic has the right to stay as she is, in the same way that some people addicted to drugs are maintained in their state by the legal prescription of their drugs, a point to which we shall return later.

Part of the difficulty encountered in working with anorectics often results from our inability or unwillingness to enter their world. We far too readily blame our clients for not 'getting better' or for being resistant to help or change. However, we are far less enthusiastic in our attempts to look inwards and to ask ourselves whether we might be responsible in any way for the therapeutic impasse, or to ascribe the lack of progress – however that is defined by each of us – to our own failure to understand.

Our failure to understand results in part from the confusion that we encounter when we attempt to define our role in relation to our clients. What are the aims of our interventions? What are our responsibilities in relation to our clients? How do we know if we have been successful or not? Unfortunately most training fails to address these questions or if it does it does so in a dogmatic way which masks the complexity of such issues.

The emphasis in much counselling training is that the aim of counselling is 'to get people better' or to 'cure' them. Such an emphasis is of course not always explicit. The choice of euphemisms to describe that which we believe we are doing when we are counselling someone is varied. However, there is often an implicit assumption that we are in fact aiming to 'cure' the individual by altering some aspects of their behaviour or cognitions which led them to seek help in the first place. If we then fail to perceive any noticeable changes in our client – for instance, they do not put on any weight – we are left feeling that we have somehow failed.

There is an important relationship between how we evaluate the outcome of our work and that which we believe to be our role. If we believe that the aim of our work is to get an anorexic client to put on weight, then if this is not achieved we may conclude that counselling has not been successful. Our sense of failure may then, for instance, lead us in some cases to cajole the client into eating. Such approaches are, with many anorexic clients, doomed to failure and are demoralising for both client and counsellor. A significant proportion of anorectics have been restricting their food intake for some time and this may have become a way of 'being-in-the-world' for them such that their behaviour will prove to be highly resistant to change. In such instances a more appropriate approach that may be adopted – which reduces the risk of alienating the client from the support they so desperately need – is to help them to lead as fulfilling a life as possible *given* their eating difficulties. This requires a difficult but essential shift in our therapeutic aims away from notions of 'cure' towards notions of management and support.

Compared to other 'disorders', what also appears to render our attempts to help the anorectic particularly difficult is that the anorexic system provides its own potent reinforcement – unlike the symptoms of other 'disorders' which seemingly hold few charms. Whilst as outside observers it may strike us that the anorectic is unhappy, it is important not to lose sight of the fact that weight loss may be her only source of pleasure and thus she has no wish to forgo this single gratification. At a time when everything else in her life feels 'messy' and confused, here she may find a way of succeeding. Perhaps more importantly, it is no longer just about being successful at something; rather it has become her solution to 'being' as an end in itself. Success becomes measurable in terms of how many pounds have been shed and provides an immediate source of positive feedback. This may perhaps help to explain why the anorectic continues to lose weight even after she has reached her original target weight.

The anorectic's response to help

The individual who is anorexic has two choices: she can either relax her control and surrender her will and thus admit defeat; or she can allow herself to die of starvation, thus gaining her paradoxical victory. This is the 'cruel trap' Palazzoli spoke of. The anorectic is highly sensitive to the precariousness of her situation and for this reason she will only with great reluctance allow anyone into her 'fortress' lest they invade it and she loses control and thus loses her 'self'. So, how is she likely to respond to attempts to 'cure' her of her symptom when it is this that she perceives to be keeping her alive? She is likely to react, as would anyone, to attempts to seemingly 'rob' her of what she not only feels is good for her but is also essential to her survival – she will reject attempts to help her. Helpers are generally perceived by her as people who are trying to coerce. The anorectic has learnt how to deal with this and she resists either by active rejection or by appearing to comply whilst feeling that she secretly knows best. An example of the latter is the weight that anorectics usually put on while receiving in-patient treatment and which they subsequently proceed to lose once they are discharged from hospital.

The benefits of self-starvation are many to the anorectic: it gives her a sense of achievement, of being better than others; it enables her to feel in control of her body and to gain the experience of being able to make her own decisions about herself; it gives her a sense of power. Ultimately and paradoxically it is only through the life of self-starvation that she feels she can be-in-the-world. Indeed it may well be that the reason why anorectics find it very difficult to accept any kind of help with their difficulties is that they feel they have found a solution which, in is own crippling way, works for them and they are understandably reluctant to give it up. It would appear that no matter what therapeutic intervention is opted for, all such endeavours will come up against the fundamental anorexic premise that thinness and control of one's body is a value of inestimable worth and something which has to be pursued and protected at all costs. If we are prepared to accept this basic notion it is also possible to understand and make perfect sense of many of the anorectic's beliefs and behaviours in the same way that granting the validity of a paranoid delusion can render a set of 'bizarre' acts intelligible.

One of my anorexic clients, Debbie (see Chapter 4), was very wary of others' attempts to help her. She often felt 'tricked' by them into eating and felt that when people said they wanted to help this meant they wanted to get her to eat. She did not trust food that was prepared by someone else as she feared they might add something fattening to it. Her need to be in control of what she ingested was reflected in the counselling relationship where she could only take in something from the sessions if she felt the insight had come from her. In other words, she would only take in and be able to use the counselling relationship if she had 'prepared' it herself in the same way she prepared her own food.

Being helped had become equated for Debbie with being deceived and she complained that people treated her 'like an idiot' who would not notice, for instance, if an extra ounce of butter was added to her meal. So any attempts on the part of others to help her were often rejected and would lead Debbie to withdraw further and to be even more distrustful of them. She felt that no one understood her, that no one really wanted to hear what she had to say but that 'others' continued to tell her what to do and how to 'be'.

Her initial distrust of me at times felt like an insurmountable obstacle. Her posture, in the early phases of our relationship, was that of an adversary defending threatened territory. It seemed important to Debbie to be allowed the time to build a bridge between her fundamental mistrust and fear of personal relationships – which had often proved to be symbiotic and destructive – and her longing for a relationship with another person who could understand her and accept her for what she felt herself to be. Although she was initially reluctant to say much to me, she gradually began to tell me her story and would often remark at the end of the session, 'I always think I'm going to come here to talk about food but I never seem to say much about it'. The fact that I did not focus on weight gain was experienced by Debbie as a relief and it ultimately enabled her to say that she did not really want to always live in this way, not because of how it made others feel, but because of how it made *her* feel.

As counsellors we need to strike a fine balance between acknowledging the precariousness of the physical state of our anorexic clients and responding to their need to 'tell their story'. This will take us far beyond the stories about food and calories which usually serve as a smokescreen for the pain and suffering to which anorexia is a solution.

If we understand anorexia as being the strategy employed by an individual struggling to protect a very precarious sense of self we may begin to appreciate that entry into the anorectic fortress is more likely to be granted if the person seeking access shows respect for it and is not set on demolishing it – even though he/she may be promising great new buildings in its place. The anorectic cannot see beyond the high wall of her fortress and it is only if she is allowed to bring its walls down herself, at her own pace, that she can begin to contemplate another life. Indeed Bruch noted that psychotherapy with ano-rectics was 'a difficult task because the false reality with which they have lived represents their only way of having experiences and patients will cling to their distorted concepts and will let go of them only slowly and reluctantly' (1988: 8). Thus the immense patience that is required when working with anorect-ics, and the threat of their possible death if they are severely emaciated, may understandably lead us to search for quick alternatives. Bearing this in mind, how can the counsellor negotiate entry into the anorectic fortress?

NEGOTIATING ENTRY INTO THE ANORECTIC FORTRESS

When I first meet with someone who presents with the anor-exic symptomatology I have two questions at the back of my mind, namely: what benefit does the individual gain from con-tinuing her attempts at self-starvation? and what would she lose if she gave up trying to lose weight? In Chapter 4 I suggested some of the answers to these questions and it is precisely these answers that, for me, point to the specific needs of the anorectic and the ways in which we might help her.

'Starting from scratch' – obstacles to listening

'I don't believe in anorexia', writes Margolis and she adds:

> The label is to help doctors and the rest of society. After all, where would they be without a definition? . . . The doctor needs the label because, without it, he would have to start from scratch. . . . He would be forced to look at the patient herself, to ask, who is this person? . . . Not a record of previous ailments, family medical history: no, a real recognition that this is a unique human being; who is moreover going to extreme lengths to assert her individuality.
>
> (1988: 47)

These are sobering words, particularly in light of the challenge that anorexia poses to those who attempt to work with it. Faced with the paradox of anorexia we may well find comfort in our theories and well-practiced techniques, for these give us a sense of direction, of knowing what to look for and what to prescribe, and thus we increase our sense of competence. However, our strict adherence to them only serves to highlight our difficulty in managing the anxiety that results from the realisation of our ignorance. We seek refuge from this in the illusion that we can understand.

Moreover, Margolis' comments point to something far deeper – that is, how our adherence to 'labels' and theories may underlie our fear of encounter as such and thus what really meeting the anorectic in her world may bring up for us. Let us not forget that the anorectic is seemingly prepared to die for her right to 'be'. Adhering to a particular theory may be our means of abstracting ourselves from the encounter by thinking of the 'other' as a label or by focusing only on certain mechanisms of behaviour. If such a technical view dominates the counselling relationship, we may well have spared ourselves a certain degree of anxiety but only at the cost of possibly missing the opportunity to engage meaningfully with our client.

Thus, if we want to meet the individual who speaks through

her relationship with food and her body and understand her, we have to be prepared to listen to what she has to say. But this understanding will not be achieved if we rely on speculation or attempt to fit her problems within a definite theory. Too often we fail to listen to our clients but rather filter everything through our preferred theoretical models. In this respect it is helpful as counsellors to attempt as far as possible to 'bracket' our beliefs, theories and assumptions about the 'why' of our client's symptoms. This way the client may be seen more clearly and hopefully with a greater degree of accuracy. The shift that this attitude towards our work makes explicit is from the line of questioning that asks 'why' to one that focuses on the 'how' and 'what' of a person's experience and that waits to hear from the client what she has to say rather than imposing the counsellor's constructions on the client's material. I am stressing the importance of *listening* to what the anorectic has to say because even though this is what coun-selling is meant to be about, the theories and assumptions we hold about the anorectic have the potential to interfere with the listening process. Indeed, it is not possible to be without theories as such – we cannot help but see the anorectic in one way or another and place our constructions on her behaviour. Nonetheless we can attempt to minimise this by focusing on descriptive questioning.

It is helpful to approach our client with a degree of curiosity, wondering about how they have managed to structure their lives in such a way as to enable them to carry on despite what we may perceive to be the maladaptiveness of their behaviour. As Hamburg has aptly pointed out, 'in deciding how to approach a symptom in psychotherapy, we need to be able to balance our respect for the architect with our compasison for the sufferer' (1989: 137).

If the counsellor wants to gain a phenomenological insight into the world of any client she must be able to transpose herself into another strange or even alien view of the world. This way she may arrive at an understanding of the client's existential position. No less is required by the anorectic. In this respect an existential counselling approach to her dilemma may be appropriate. Existential counselling does not concern itself with causes but rather with being-in-the-world. It tries to view phenomena in a direct way that is not disturbed by a preoccupation with underlying causes. 'What' the client is experiencing is the primary concern of the counsellor. 'Why' she experiences things as she does is only of secondary importance. By virtue of the emphasis placed on seeing, as far as possible, the world of the client through her eyes, the existential approach avoids the pitfalls of interpretative approaches which rely on telling the anorectic 'why' she feels in a particular way. But how can we avoid this trap? I would like to suggest remembering three rules which are part of what is referred to as the 'phenomenological' method of enquiry (see Spinelli 1989) as we being a session with a client, namely:

1 Bracket your immediate expectations and assumptions so that you can focus on what the client is telling you.

2 Retain your observations at a descriptive level as opposed to an analytic level. Try to refrain from immediately imposing upon what your client tells you a particular significance or hypothesis.

3 Avoid attributing greater value or significance to particular aspects of your client's story. For instance, if your client tells you they have not had a relationship for some time this is not necessarily more important than when she tells you she gets angry when the weather is unstable. Such statements merely reflect your client's experience of different dimensions of her world and merit exploration in their own right.

Although these rules are straightforward enough – and are helpful guidelines irrespective of our theoretical allegiances – we need only take ourselves back to the last session with a client (even to the notes we made after the session) to realise that we attributed more significance to particular aspects of what the client told us. But why was this? To whom was that important? And what led us, say, to attribute more importance to the client's statements about her family and not her next-door neighbour? To what extent were our interventions influenced by our own assumptions about the problems the individual facing us had rather than what the client may have been telling us about her problems?

It is very difficult to put these rules into practice but we can at least attempt to do so. Whilst we can never be totally theory-free, we can be aware of the immediate barriers that we impose against this. We can begin to reflect on the anxieties and fears that may lie behind our need to 'know' why our client feels in a particular way without ever really questioning whether our interpretations are perhaps more like smokescreens than aids to clarification. By confronting honestly our biases and limitations we open ourselves to the possibility of engaging with our client in a dialogue. This very notion implies the bi-directional nature of the counselling process whereby both counsellor and client affect and are affected by each other. It is only by engaging in such a process that we can truly meet the individual facing us and understand the meaning their anorexia holds for them.

The assessment session

Whilst it is important to let your client lead the way it is also helpful for you to get some information about the extent of your client's eating problem at the assessment stage. The information you elicit will enable you to make a decision as to whether you feel able to help the client or whether a referral to another colleague would be more suitable.

At the initial meeting it is helpful to get an idea of the methods of weight control your client uses. It is also important to gain some idea of how much or how little food they consume. For instance, if your client tells you that they binge invite them to specify what a 'binge' consists of. Some will feel very ashamed to tell you and it is important to be sensitive to this. However, you may also discover that they have a very distorted perception of what constitutes a binge and this may alert you to some of the reference points by which they judge their own sense of self-worth.

Frequently the anorectic's previous experience of discussing her eating habits and ways of controlling her weight will have been a negative one which has led to highly charged emotional exchanges with families, partners and other professionals. This will have contributed to their reluctance to share such information with others for fear that they will simply be told to eat. It is thus important that you communicate an attitude of acceptance to your client and acknowledge the desperation and courage which are both aspects of their attempt to find a way of being-in-the-world through self-starvation and other methods of weight control.

A balance needs to be struck to avoid overwhelming the client with questions about her eating habits, for asking too many questions may lead her to feel exposed too soon and this may then lead her to feel out of control of the situation – something she will be highly sensitive to. It is difficult, yet important, to find a balance as this will determine whether you can establish a working alliance with your client.

Developing a working alliance

Anorexia in many ways represents an attempt at self-sufficiency. It is an extreme assertion that nothing or no one is needed. As a counsellor this will be one of the main obstacles to helping your client. First sessions often focus on the client's feelings about seeking help and the implications of acknowledging her needs for her self-perception. The acknowledgement of needs may feel very threatening to the individual and it frequently serves to confirm their sense that they are a 'mess' and not in control of their lives after all. This may then lead them to assuage such anxieties by restricting their eating even further, thereby reasserting their tenuous hold on their lives.

The client may have many fantasies about what you will think of her. Will you think she is a 'mess' or 'greedy' if she confesses that she has had two apples instead of one? It is important to explore such anxieties and to gradually work towards a reframing of the problem not solely in terms of the difficulties around eating but in terms of the client's difficulty in letting someone help her, as this is frequently experienced as a surrender of control.

A strong working alliance is an important prerequisite for change. It does however take time to develop and your commitment and integrity may be put to a severe test. Sessions may be missed with no explanation given. You may be accused of not understanding even if you may feel that you have done your best to do so. Working with an anorectic requires developing a very particular kind of attunement to the client's needs, as a mother does with her developing infant – too many questions and interpretations and she may feel overfed; too little response and she may feel unable to reach out. Inevitably mistakes will be made and this is part of the process; rather than be discouraged by them we need to learn from them to help us to better understand our client. This is where our own supervision and support become very important.

The difficulties frequently encountered at the very early stages of the relationship between client and counsellor argue strongly against establishing fixed contracts. There are several reasons for this. Firstly, it may leave the client feeling that you are the one in control. Secondly, it may lead her to panic at the thought of having to resolve her difficulties in a very limited period of time; we thereby increase the risk of confirming her deep-rooted sense of failure when she finds she is unable to achieve what she set out to achieve. It is important never to lose sight of the fact that for many anorectics this may have become their way of managing their lives over many months if not years. Thirdly, setting time-limited contracts and targets may lead us as counsellors to be more likely to adopt a directive approach when we realise how unlikely it is that our client will 'get better' by the agreed date. This is unlikely to be helpful. Rather it may simply lead the client to feel that, yet again, someone else is in charge of her decisions and her life.

A solid working alliance can more easily be achieved if from the first session you offer the client the space to tell you her story. Careful attention should be given to the individual's description of their distress rather than attempting to fit what the client tells you into pre-existing assumptions and beliefs about 'why' the anorectic feels as she does.

Your client's distress about her eating behaviour, weight and appearance should all be taken seriously. It is important that you accept the individual's beliefs about her shape and weight as genuine. With time it will also be important to challenge her beliefs – but it is best to wait until you have established a good working alliance with your client before you do so. Reassuring the client, appealing to their will-power or concentrating on achieving an ideal weight are all likely to alienate them because these do not address the deeper problems to which the anorexia is a solution.

A major obstacle to establishing a working alliance with an anorexic client is, as has been previously mentioned, the anorectic's resistance, resentment and defiance which may elicit very strong negative reactions in the counsellor. These need to be carefully monitored and explored in supervision so as to not allow them to lead to retaliatory responses on your part. Whatever our level of expertise and skill supervision remains essential, although the form that this takes may well change as our experience grows.

Letting the client take the lead: the problem with interpretations

A number of approaches to counselling rely on the use of interpretation to facilitate the client's insight into their problems. However the use of interpretation when working with anorectics deserves special consideration. The process of offering an interpretation represents a dynamic the anorectic will only be too familiar with, namely that someone else 'knows' how she feels but that she herself does not know or feel. It serves to confirm their deep-seated fear that they are incompetent, that they have no control over their lives and are doomed to dependence not only on their families but now also on the counsellor. The client, in turn, relies on compliance and gives the counsellor what he or she wants. Many anorectics have read widely on the topic of anorexia and once they know where a counsellor stands ideologically they tend to become 'perfect clients', thereby perpetuating an unhelpful interaction with the counsellor.

Hilde Bruch, who has written extensively on anorexia, advocated a 'fact-finding, non-interpretative approach', which relied on the counsellor's 'constructive use of ignorance', requiring the counsellor to suspend his or her knowledge and expertise and permitting the client to express what she experiences without attempting to explain it or label it. This kind of collaborative work with the counsellor was felt by Bruch to offer the anorectic a new experience – the experience of being listened to and not being told by someone else what she 'really' feels or means.

Bruch stressed the need for the anorectic to do the 'uncovering' in the therapeutic work and understood the task of the counsellor as that of assisting clients in uncovering their own abilities for thinking, feeling and judging. Her emphasis on the counsellor's task as that of 'assisting' is very important. If we can offer our client this type of counselling relationship the anorectic is more likely to become an active participant in the counselling process. This way she may be helped to feel safe enough to relinquish or modify the symptom that until now gave her the experience of being in charge of her life. She may then begin to discover her undeveloped and untapped resources, and become alert and alive to what is going on within herself. These are necessary steps for her developing autonomy, initiative and responsibility for her life.

As I mentioned in Chapter 4, engulfment is experienced as a risk in being understood and in view of the anorectic's fear of engulfment it is not surprising that an interpretation may be experienced as an invasion. As Laing pointed out, one way used to preserve identity under pressure from the threat of engulfment is to isolate oneself, to withdraw. Indeed this is the anorectic's most likely response to an interpretation as this mobilises her anxiety, for to be 'understood correctly is to be engulfed ... drowned, eaten up, smothered, stifled in or by another person's supposed all-embracing comprehension' (Laing 1960: 45).

Thus it seems reasonable to suppose that the counsellor's attempts to tell the anorectic about herself, to explain her behaviour to her, will be felt to be invasive and wounding. They are therefore likely to be rejected. If anorexia is, as I have suggested, an attempt to assert autonomy by an individual whose sense of self is precarious, then to be told by the counsellor, yet again, who she is and what she should be is likely to be unhelpful and damaging. A number of anorectics with whom I have worked, and others whom I have met informally, have reported their experiences of being told 'who, what and why I was' and confirmed that this was an unhelpful intervention on the part of the counsellor or therapist.

Laura (see Chapter 4) was very sensitive to any deviations from the non-interpretative approach I was trying to use in my work with her. On one occasion I interpreted something Laura had said. She missed the three subsequent sessions without giving me any reason. It later transpired that my interpretation had alienated her. What seemed to be important was not so much whether the interpretation had been 'correct' or not but how, by interpreting something, I had deprived Laura of an opportunity to discover herself at her own pace. Indeed when she returned to our sessions three weeks later she spoke of how her family had always 'bombarded' her with their selfish needs, that she had always done what others wanted her to do, but that she had never been listened to. This was undoubtedly a critique of me as a real person who through my interpretation had perpetuated Laura's experience of being 'bombarded' by other's needs – in this instance my own needs. It had been experienced by her – as we later discussed together – as though she had been 'force-fed' by me. My acknowledgement of my own mistake seemed to enable Laura to experience a new kind of relationship, one that perhaps merited her trust and co-operation.

The task of counselling the anorectic is more than anything else the task of translating the symptoms of anorexia into the reality and details of her everyday life. This involves understanding the myriad ways in which anorexia enhances or interferes with the client's life: what can she do now that she could not do before or, conversely, what limitations are now imposed on her life? This is a further example of how a counselling approach rooted in the here-and-now experience of being-in-the-world may be most fruitful for working with anorectics. This focus enables the counsellor to gain an insight into the anorectic's world which does not necessitate reconstructing from the past.

There are several reasons why it is important for the anorectic to tell us in detail what her world is like. For many anorectics the counsellor may be yet another person whom they feel will not be able to understand them. Their previous experience of attempting to relate to others what and how they feel may have left them feeling misunderstood, ridiculed or labelled as 'mad'.

Ann, another of my anorexic clients, was 31. She had had an eating problem since she was 14. However, she became particularly concerned about her weight when she became pregnant at the age of 24. She regularly went without any food (with the exception of some yoghurt and fruit) for three to four consecutive days following which she would then occasionally binge. She described how she had never been able to tell anyone what she felt when she ingested food that she perceived to be 'fattening' – it made her feel as though her mouth was being cut up and was bleeding. She was concerned that no one would understand this. On those rare occasions when she had found the courage to explain to her family how she felt she was told to 'pull herself together' and that she should think about the millions of starving people in the world. In counselling it was important for Ann to be able to describe her experiences in great detail, to really explore what the blood in her mouth felt like and to be sure that I understood what she meant without judging or labelling her. This, she admitted, had been her greatest fear and what had prevented her from seeking help any sooner.

The anorectic needs to know that we understand how difficult her life is. She can only be sure that we understand if she herself has told us through the detailed exploration and description of her life in the here-and-now. She will not necessarily assume that we understand her preoccupation with food, or that we can even begin to conceive how frightening her relationships with others have become and how staying thin is more important than anyone or anything else. She may assume we cannot understand any of this because she fears that her relationship with us will be equally threatening, that we will also try to force-feed her or trick her into eating and thus relinquishing her power. If this is the case she will be relieved when she realises that we are not going to do any of these things but that we are instead going to ask her permission to enter her world on her terms.

Negotiating goals

The counselling work should proceed at the client's pace and not the counsellor's. This may prove difficult if working within multidisciplinary teams where the priorities of other professionals – who may often have more 'power' than the individual counsellor – may dictate how long the client may be seen for and hence the pace at which the work may be carried out. Bearing in mind such constraints it is nonetheless important to acknowledge and communicate to your client that 'getting better' or being 'cured' is not just synonymous with achieving a given weight. Rather you need to communicate to your client that what matters is how she feels about herself and her world and that improvement can only, in the final analysis, be measured against what she values, which may not be what you or society as a whole, value.

In negotiating goals I have found it is important to share with the client my understanding that the symptoms of anorexia have an adaptive function. It is best to adopt a deconstructive rather than a destructive approach to your client's symptoms, thereby acknowledging their protective power whilst also pointing out the cost to the client's life and well-being. This will help the client to feel reassured that you are not going to force them to eat too much too soon.

The counselling frame

Counselling does not take place in a vacuum. It happens not only within a given cultural and 'theoretical' framework but also within a given physical environment with specific rules which underlie particular expectations of the client and the counsellor. For example there may be an expectation that the client arrives on time and that the session finishes at an agreed time, that the counsellor sees the client in the same room at the same time each week and that the counsellor will be bound by certain rules of confidentiality. Clearly, institutional settings restrict the amount of responsibility that individual practitioners can exercise over the therapeutic frame that they can offer their clients. Hence, some counsellors may be forced to change rooms frequently or they may be bound to share the content of their sessions with other professionals who may hold clinical responsibility for the client. Such restrictions may severely interfere with the counselling process and lead to intrusive deviations from what might otherwise be regarded as a 'good-enough', safe therapeutic frame within which the client may begin to trust the counsellor.

However, whatever the setting in which we practice, deviations are likely to occur and it is important that they are acknowledged, even if they cannot be altogether avoided. For instance, if working with an adolescent, her parents may be paying for her sessions and may want to know what is happening and so a third party may become involved in a relationship that is meant to be confidential. Although it is easy to get involved in discussions with the parents and to view this as part of your role, anorexic clients are particularly sensitive to such intrusions and these will interfere with your relationship. The client is likely to feel that you cannot be trusted. Anorectics have difficulty in experiencing themselves as the uncontested authors of their lives. They often feel that they are merely following a script that has been handed down to them by an 'other' who knows better than them how they should lead their lives. If parents become involved – albeit indirectly by paying for the fees or by contacting the counsellor – this will contribute to the client's experience that they are not in charge of their lives, that nothing is solely theirs. Such issues need to be explored within the counselling relationship.

If working with adolescent anorectics who are still living at home it is important to consider the suitability of family therapy. The latter has been shown to be an effective intervention with younger clients and serves to communicate that the problem is not located in the individual but rather that it may be understood as a response to a particular family system. It also circumvents some of the problems around boundaries that may arise if only the adolescent is seen for counselling. Frequently the parents also need support and family therapy can be an effective way of taking everybody's needs into account. This is particularly relevant when working privately as you are less likely to have the support of other professionals who could work with the parents whilst you see the adolescent. If the parents' anxieties remain uncontained this increases the likelihood that they will intrude into their childrens' counselling.

In the light of the above observations it is important that what is offered to the client is negotiated first and preferably only with the client, whose sensitivity to the implications of the intrusion of others into the counselling relationship should be validated by an honest acknowledgement by the counsellor. Such validations will frequently be experienced as very therapeutic as they may represent one of the few occasions in the person's life when their judgement of what is 'good' for them has been heard.

The anorectic is particularly sensitive to the boundaries of the counselling relationship. In order to understand her experience it is helpful to view the therapeutic hour as though it were a meal. For the anorectic, meals are highly structured events. She will probably spend several hours planning what she will eat, down to the last calorie. It is often important, as I pointed out earlier, that she has prepared her own meal. If eating with others, it may at times be hard to sit through a whole meal. She may fear being asked to eat more or she may fear that *she* will want to eat more unless she physically removes herself from the table. The acknowledgement of her hunger is highly threatening to her as it will have become symbolically equated with the acknowledgement of her needs and these remind her that she is not in control.

If we transpose the above observations to the counselling relationship we can gain some helpful insights. It will be important to the anorectic that she feels in control of the counselling relationship and of how much she can take in at any one time. She is thus likely to be highly sensitive to deviations from the therapeutic boundaries such as extending the session, even if only by a few minutes, as this may lead her to feel over-fed. Or she may herself establish her own boundaries which may require some adaptation on the part of the counsellor.

Sue, another client I worked with, finished the session each week a few minutes before I would say it was time. As she got up to leave I would simply remind her that she had some time left. I never made any interpretations about this but it was important to acknowledge that I was clear about my boundaries, even though it was her prerogative to leave when she wanted. It was only several months later that Sue remarked on this particular pattern and it was only then, bearing in mind the comments I made earlier about the use of interpretation, that I added my own thoughts about this pattern. By leaving the session early before I called time Sue was attempting to retain some control in a situation which she experienced as very threatening. Just as she had described her fear at the dinner table with her parents who would insist that she should eat more, she feared that if she stayed till the end of the session I might also try to force-feed her. With time Sue became able to stay till the end of our sessions.

Working with other professionals

As anorexia is in many instances associated with physical problems it increases the likelihood that the counsellor will be working alongside other professionals. This can be a very supportive and enriching experience. However it may also give rise to conflict as the aims of professionals can vary both within and between professional groups. At times the client may become the victim in a battle of differing beliefs about the nature of anorexia and differing therapeutic aims. It will be important for the counsellor to be clear about their own role and to whom they feel responsible: is it the client, the institution they work for or the person who has clinical responsibility for the client? There are no simple answers to such questions but it part of our responsibility to our client to reflect on these issues.

When working within a public health service setting it is likely that medical responsibility for the client will be held by a consultant psychiatrist who will need to be informed of your work and the client's progress. The client's progress may also be discussed at review meetings and their medical notes may be read by other professionals. This means that there will be inevitable deviations with regards to the confidentiality of the counselling relationship. Clients are highly sensitive to any deviations in the expected confidentiality of their relationship with their counsellor. It is important to acknowledge the implications for the client of any intrusion in the counselling relationship by third parties. Their feelings about this may not be necessarily voiced explicitly but through the stories clients tell us they are often giving us disguised messages about their experience of the counselling relationship. They may be telling us, for instance, stories about people not doing their job properly or they may remember that when they were younger their mother looked through their diaries without seeking their permission. Whilst such stories clearly represent issues that are of concern to the client, their recollection is also triggered by the here-and-now situation with the counsellor and can thus be seen – as in the example of the diaries – to also contain a communication to the counsellor about the client's experience of the lack of confidentiality.

If working in private practice the counsellor has more freedom to determine with whom they share any information about their client. Some counsellors contact the client's GP – with their clients' consent – as a matter of course to inform them of their involvement. The implications of this for the confidentiality of the counselling relationship need to be carefully considered and discussed with the client. Conscious consent by the client does not necessarily mean that this is something they are happy with but it is unlikely that the client will raise their objections to this explicitly. We thus need to be sensitive to our clients' more indirect communications which can alert us to how they actually feel about the GP being informed. It is also important to question our own need to contact the GP – for whose benefit is it? Notwithstanding such considerations, as we have seen, there may be situations when the counsellor may decide to seek medical assistance. The usual route for this would be to contact the client's GP who will then make a decision as to whether anyone else needs to be involved. If such a course of action seems appropriate the client should nonetheless be consulted first.

DISCUSSION ISSUES

1 What specific difficulties do you think you might encounter when working with anorexic clients? How might you be able to overcome these?

2 When working with an anorexic client what would your aims be? How would you know if you had been able to achieve these aims?

3 What would you consider yourself responsible for in relation to an anorexic client?

6

The Rights of the Anorectic and the Counsellor's Dilemmas

There is little doubt that working with someone who is anorexic, particularly if they are severely emaciated, raises a number of ethical dilemmas for the counsellor. By its very nature anorexia has great power to disturb those who attempt to help the anorectic. This power stems from two sources, namely the potentially life-threatening nature of anorexia and the challenge it can pose to the counsellor's personal beliefs about the importance of being thin.

WHOSE ANXIETY IS IT ANYWAY? – SOME BOUNDARY ISSUES

It is not easy to watch someone wasting away before our very eyes. However, our own anxieties, which may lead us to act in ways that are not always necessarily 'therapeutic', may arise because we may be feeling unclear about the extent of our responsibility in relation to the individual who self-starves. Even if we appreciate the anorectic's anxieties surrounding weight gain and want to support her in overcoming these, as counsellors it is also important that we clarify our own position in relation to the physical safety of the client.

Counsellors vary with regard to the extent of a client's weight loss which they are prepared to work with. This may be less of an issue for those already working within a medical setting where it is likely that such decisions will be taken by a consultant. If working privately and your client is at or below 60–5 per cent of Average Expected Body Weight (AEBW) you will soon be finding yourself with a medical emergency on your hands. At a weight level of 50 per cent of AEBW the individual will die unless she eats. However, it is medically safe to work with someone who is at 75 per cent of AEBW, even though the medical consensus is that an individual is not 'cured' if her weight is restored only up to this level.

Our own anxieties may be alleviated if we carefully think through the limits of our responsibility as counsellors. For instance, is it our responsibility if our client dies because we have not sought medical assistance? Conversely, what 'right' do we have to breach the confidentiality of the counselling relationship and contact the client's GP even against her wishes? Bearing in mind that many counsellors will not be faced with such extremes of behaviour we need nonetheless to consider such ethical dilemmas.

A way in which we may practically translate what we feel responsible for in relation to the individual who self-starves is in terms of the weight level below which we would not be prepared to work without also organising medical support. Whilst it is also important to bear in mind that within the private setting the referrals we are likely to receive may not appear to be as serious as those just described, it is far from unknown for an anorectic to continue losing weight even if she is receiving counselling or therapy.

As I have repeatedly stressed, more often than not the anorexic individual will not perceive their self-starvation as problematic. Rather what is experienced as problematic are other people's attempts to interfere with the individual's dieting. However, if the self-starvation progresses unabated it may lead to death (see Chapter 2). This raises the difficult question of whether the anorectic's mental state is such that her self-starvation may be considered to be rational and self-directed. The prevailing view is that the anorectic's actions are actually out of control and irrational. It is on the basis of such views that the anorectic's compulsory admission to hospital is sanctioned under the Mental Health Act 1983 when there is a possible threat to the individual's life. Once admitted to hospital the anorectic may be force-fed (e.g. intravenously) and may be subjected to a variety of treatment programmes whose principal aim is to restore the anorectic to a 'normal' weight.

A course of action such as that described above may at first appear to be justified in order to save a life. However it also raises important ethical issues which arise whenever compulsory admission to a hospital is enforced. Such issues are thus not specifically related to anorexia and there are no simple solutions to questions of such philosophical and therapeutic importance.

It may however be worth considering the following. There are a number of 'decisions' that people make in their lives, or behaviours that people engage in, which have the potential to be life-threatening. Not all of them can lead to the individual being compulsorily admitted to a hospital to receive treatment against their will. For instance, excessive alcohol consumption can lead to death. However, someone who is known to drink excessively over a period of years will not be compulsorily detained to help them recover from their alcohol addiction. So why does one individual seemingly have the 'right' to kill themselves and another is considered to be irrational and not in a position to make her own decisions about her life? Such inconsistencies are clearly worrying and confuse further a very contentious area of discourse. Nonetheless, these are issues that may well arise in the course of your work with anorectics. Whilst there are no guidelines as to what you should or should not do if you are working privately and are not bound by the policies of a particular institution, it is certainly important to consider such ethical issues before you actually encounter them. It is also important to take your concerns to your supervisor. If you are working within an institution such problems are circumvented as you will have clear guidelines about procedures that need to be followed. For some this will ease some of the anxieties that may be triggered when considering such ethical issues. For others the discrepancy between their own personal values and institutional policies may raise even further problems.

It may feel difficult and punitive having to tell a client that if she falls below a certain weight you feel you can only continue to work with her if she also seeks medical assistance. However, this is not necessarily a punitive stance. We are not asking the client to restore her weight to her AEBW – something which many anorectics would find extremely difficult. We are merely acknowledging that if she falls below a certain weight and does not receive medical help she might die.

Often the client may express anger at your setting of limits and may initially feel that you do not understand her and thereby feel rejected. However she may also feel contained in knowing that you are clear about how far you are prepared to accompany her along the path of self-starvation. Ducker and Slade (1988) have described the anorectic as often being caught in a 'whirlpool of starvation' whereby she may have no sense that she can stop. By offering her clear boundaries you may be providing her with a space within which she may not necessarily be forced to resume her AEBW but where she will know that she is not going to die.

If in the course of your work your client shows signs of continuing to lose weight this fact needs to be addressed. Whilst some counsellors may feel uneasy about sharing their own anxieties regarding a client's weight loss, we need not necessarily be reluctant to do so, as long as our anxiety is well grounded and informed and as long as we are consistent and not overwhelmed with panic. Indeed, it is not necessarily appropriate for a counsellor to remain unconcerned where their client's weight is at or below 65 per cent of AEBW and she is still cutting back on food. In such a situation it would be appropriate for the counsellor to share their anxiety as a fact relating directly to the client's deteriorating condition. This is a fact that needs to be communicated to the client in a straightforward manner that shows awareness of their feelings. For instance, you may tell your client that whilst you know that they have been feeling good about their weight loss, you are concerned because they have continued to lose weight and you wonder whether there are times when they also feel concerned but are finding it difficult to eat. It is important to own your anxieties while also opening up the possibility for the client to acknowledge that she is also very concerned about her well-being and safety but that she cannot see any other way of managing her life.

'I COULD DO WITH A BIT OF ANOREXIA MYSELF'

The dilemmas that result from the potentially life-threatening nature of anorexia are however not the only challenge that anorexia poses to counsellors. By its very nature anorexia also challenges the counsellor's personal beliefs, as the ordinary values that many people cherish play an important part in creating a potentially life-threatening condition. Female counsellors in particular are likely to find that they share some, if not all, of the anorectic's values and aspirations regarding food regulation and self-control. It is not infrequent to hear female professionals in this field saying in passing 'I could do with a bit of anorexia myself'. Such comments are frequently laughed off but perhaps they warrant closer examination as they suggest a remarkable – and perhaps uncomfortable – similarity between those actions valued by the anorectic and those many of us also value.

Our attempts to help the anorectic may be undermined if we fail to listen to ourselves and to challenge the extent to which our own cultural background may have led us to acquire many of the values and beliefs about the importance of body shape and weight control that the anorectic so poignantly expresses through her self-starvation.

Recognising the similarities between ourselves and our clients is not easy. It can be disconcerting to realise the extent to which the anorectic's extreme actions grow out of 'ordinary' values that we tend to take for granted. At times it may be easier to think of the pain and confusion our clients present us with as resulting from an illness. Such a conceptualisation of anorexia may reassure us and in many respects also serves to absolve us and the rest of society for having caused the person's behaviour – if it's an illness it's not our business, as it were. The idea of anorexia as an illness might not only serve to justify intervention without consent, but also to distance us from that which we find disturbing. We may thus find comfort in the theories that implicate a yet unspecified endocrine disturbance or individual 'psychopathology'. However, we do so at the cost of never really understanding our anorexic client.

DISCUSSION ISSUES

1 Under what conditions, if any, would you refer an anorexic client for in-patient treatment? Would such a decision raise any conflicts for you?

2 Do you think that the anorectic's psychological state is such that she is in a position to make a decision about whether she wants to starve herself to death?

3 Counsellors working with anorectics are likely to find that they share many of their values and aspirations regarding

the importance of being slim and of self-control. Is this an area you might find problematic? How would you deal with this if working with an anorexic client?

7

Conclusion

To be or not to be

Throughout this book, I have referred to the individual who opts for a life of self-starvation as the 'anorectic' and to what she suffers from as 'anorexia nervosa'. Such a diagnostic label, however, explains very little and merely reduces the individual to her symptoms. Debbie, Laura, Ann, Sheila McLeod and Karen Margolis are but a few amongst many who reveal through their apparent pursuit of thinness a desperate attempt to cope with life and its paradoxes, a task rendered all the more difficult because of their insecurity about their very existence. The diagnostic label obscures their plight.

It is not easy to reach a state where one no longer needs food. But, above all, this is a state the anorectic is prepared to die for. As Valerie Valère, who was herself anorexic, writes:

> One cannot, from one day to the next, no longer know hunger, not need anything more, that's wrong! It is a form of training, an aim: no longer being like all the others, no longer being enslaved to the physical and material demands of the world: I think this route leads to another world: pure, without rubbish or pollution.
>
> (1978: 43)

If the anorectic's choice not to eat, followed to its inevitable conclusion, leads her to her own death it is, nonetheless, a search for another life. This human being is one that is seeking to be born. Anorexia is in many ways a self-protective mechanism which is born of the anorectic's sense of the precariousness of her ontological status. It is an attempt to create and conquer internally what she feels is impossible to conquer and control in the world around her.

Conclusion

Alienated from the natural and public world, the anorectic retreats into her anorexia where she can find temporary relief, all along trying to preserve a sense of 'self'. Within the context of such a fragile existence it is perhaps not surprising to find that the anorectic experiences difficulties throughout all the dimensions of her world. If we are interested in the aetiology of anorexia we need to address ourselves to how an individual develops such a precarious sense of identity whereby she is overwhelmed by the basic existential 'givens' that we are all confronted with and have to make some sense of, and retreats into an existence that is no longer open to its existential possibilities.

Counselling may be a way of helping the individual trapped in the anorectic fortress to step outside it and negotiate a different life on her own terms. In this context her anorexia will benefit from being understood as an attempt at self-realisation in a world of her own, as a means of coming to terms with that world. In this sense anorexia can be said to be an existential solution for a being who cannot find any other way of being-in-the-world than through self-starvation.

Within such a framework it is easier to appreciate why men as well as women may opt for a life of self-starvation. Such a conceptualisation of anorexia is less problematic, for instance, than those positioning anorexia as a response to the threat of womanhood and sexuality or as a response to the prerogatives of a patriarchal society. Both these positions have been argued convincingly in specific instances. However, they both present difficulties in the case of the male anorectic who must presumably be responding to the threat of emergent manhood. Again, this may be the case for some anorexic men but it is unlikely to offer a complete picture in every instance. These difficulties illustrate the need to see anorexia within the wider context of human existence and what it means to be-in-the-world for human beings; in this context the anxieties and conflicts of men and women alike will be understood as more similar than dissimilar. Clearly there is a need to ask specific questions about particular groups. In addressing the social construction of the female body I pointed out how this dimension might critically affect the woman's experience of her body and how it might feed into her anxieties and fears, in a way that would not apply to a man's experience of his body.

As one surveys the literature on anorexia it becomes clear – as I hope this book will have conveyed to you – that there are no definite answers, no infallible techniques that can assist us in our attempts to help the anorectic. Many factors interact to produce such a disabling – yet for the anorectic paradoxically empowering – condition. The contribution that counselling can make to the life of the anorectic is debatable. This, however, should not discourage us as it applies to all the problems that we are confronted with in our daily practices. It is desirable to entertain a healthy scepticism about the impact of counselling lest we become complacent and give in to omnipotent fantasies about what we can or should achieve.

As I have also emphasised in this book, anorexia largely remains in the realms of medicine and its allied branch – psychiatry. Here the anorectic is labelled and the anorexia becomes her 'illness', something she must be 'cured' of. The question of 'cure' in anorexia is a controversial issue. By and large, when 'cure' is considered the most important criterion appears to be weight gain. However, the individual who cannot find any other way to be-in-the-world but through a life of self-starvation is not necessarily 'cured' when she starts to eat again. Just as the origins of anorexia do not lie in weight loss, so recovery does not reside in its gain. At the end of her counselling the anorectic may not necessarily be 'cured' in the medical or psychiatric sense of the word. To obtain biological recovery is not an impossible task. However to enable the anorectic to step out of her 'Golden Cage' remains a very challenging and rewarding one – one that as Sheila McLeod painfully realised requires no less than the reassessment of a whole life. In our attempts to help the anorectic achieve this we may well benefit from reminding ourselves that, as Joseph Conrad said, 'strictly speaking, the question is not how to get cured but how to live'.

Further Reading

Bruch, Hilde (1979), *The Golden Cage*, New York: Vintage Books.

—— (1988), *Conversations with Anorexics*, New York: Basic Books.

Brumberg, Joan J. (1988), *Fasting Girls*, Cambridge, Mass.: Harvard University Press.

Gordon, Richard A. (1990), *Anorexia and Bulimia: Anatomy of a Social Epidemic*, Oxford: Blackwell.

Orbach, Susie (1986), *Hunger Strike*, London: Faber & Faber.

Palazzoli, Mara Selvini (1974), *Self-Starvation*, Sussex: Human Context Books.

References

CHAPTER 1

Bell, R. (1985), *Holy Anorexia*, Chicago: University of Chicago Press.

Brumberg, J.J. (1988), *Fasting Girls*, Cambridge, Mass.: Harvard University Press.

Freud, S. (1895), *Pre-psychoanalytic Publications and Unpublished Drafts*, in J. Strachey (ed.), *Standard Edition of the Complete Psychological Works of Sigmund Freud*, London: Hogarth Press.

Goiten, P. (1942), 'The potential prostitute: the role of anorexia in the defence against prostitution desires', *Journal of Criminal Psychopathology*, vol. 2: 359–67.

Morton, R. (1694), *Phthisiologica: or a Treatise of Consumptions*, London: Smith & Walford.

Waller, J.V., Kaufman, M.R. and Deutsch, F. (1940), 'Anorexia nervosa, a psychosomatic entity', *Psychosomatic Medicine*, vol. 2: 3–16.

CHAPTER 2

McLelland, L., Mynors-Wallis, L. and Treasure, J. (1991), 'Sexual abuse, disordered personality and eating problems', *British Journal of Psychiatry*, vol. 158(10): 63–8.

Russell, G.F.M. (1979), 'Bulimia nervosa: an ominous variant of anorexia nervosa', *Psychological Medicine*, vol. 9: 429–48.

CHAPTER 3

Andersen, A.E. (1990), 'Diagnosis and treatment of males with eating disorders', in A.E. Andersen (ed.), *Males with Eating Disorders*, New York: Brunner/Mazel.

Bruch, H. (1973), *Eating and Disorders: Obesity, Anorexia Nervosa and the Person Within*, New York: Basic Books.

—— (1979), *The Golden Cage*, New York: Vintage Books.

References

—— (1982), 'Anorexia nervosa: therapy and theory', *American Journal of Psychology*, vol. 139: 1531–8.

Brumberg, J. (1988), *Fasting Girls*, Cambridge, Mass.: Harvard University Press.

Di Nicola, V. (1990), 'Anorexia multiforme: self-starvation in historical and cultural context', *Transcultural Psychiatric Research Review*, vol. 27(4).

Herzog, D.B., Bradburn, I.S. and Newman, K. (1990), 'Sexuality in males with eating problems', in A.E. Andersen (ed.), *Males with Eating Disorders*, New York: Brunner/Mazel.

Hill, A.J. and Oliver, S. (1992), 'Eating in the adult world: the rise of dieting in childhood and adolescence', *British Journal of Clinical Psychology*, vol. 31(1): 95–104.

Minuchin, S., Rosman, B. and Baker, L. (1978), *Psychosomatic Families: Anorexia Nervosa in Context*, Cambridge, Mass.: Harvard University Press.

Mumford, D.B., Whitehouse, A.M. and Plattes, M. (1991), 'Sociocultural correlates of eating disorders among Asian schoolgirls in Bradford', *British Journal of Psychiatry*, vol. 158: 222–8.

Raimbault, G. and Eliacheff, C. (1989), *Les Indomptables: figures de l'anorexie*, Paris: Odile Jacob.

Scott, D. (1986), 'Anorexia nervosa in the male', *International Journal of Eating Disorders*, vol. 5: 799–819.

Yager, J., Kurtzman, F., Landswerk, J. and Wiesmeier, E. (1988), 'Behaviours and attitude related to eating disorders in homosexual male college students', *American Journal of Psychiatry*, vol. 145: 495–7.

CHAPTER 4

Beauvoir, S. de (1949), *The Second Sex*, London: Picador.

Binswanger, L. (1968), *Being in the World*, trans. J. Needleman, London: Souvenir Press.

Boss, M. (1955), *Introduction à la médecine psychosomatique*, Paris: PUF.

Bruch, H. (1979), *The Golden Cage*, New York: Vintage Books.

Deurzen-Smith, E. van (1988), *Existential Counselling in Practice*, London: Sage.

Edwards, G. (1987), 'Anorexia and the family', in M. Lawrence (ed.), *Fed Up and Hungry*, London: Women's Press.

Laing, R.D. (1960), *The Divided Self*, London: Pelican Books.

Margolis, K. (1988), *To Eat or Not to Eat*, London: Camden Press.

McLeod, S. (1981), *The Art of Starvation*, London: Virago.

Palazzoli, M.S. (1974), *Self-Starvation*, Sussex: Human Context Books.

Pennycook, Wyl (1987), 'Anorexia and adolescence', in M. Lawrence (ed.), *Fed Up and Hungry*, London: Women's Press.

Yalom, I. (1980), *Existential Psychotherapy*, New York: Basic Books.

References

CHAPTER 5

Bruch, H. (1979), *The Golden Cage*, New York: Vintage Books.
—— (1988), *Conversations with Anorexics*, New York: Basic Books.
Hamburg, P. (1989), 'Bulimia: the construction of a symptom', in J. Bemporad and D. Herzog (eds), *Psychoanalysis and Eating Disorders*, New York: Guildford Press.
Laing, R.D. (1960), *The Divided Self*, London: Pelican Books.
Margolis, K. (1988), *To Eat or Not to Eat*, London: Camden Press.
Palazzoli, M.S. (1974), *Self-Starvation*, Sussex: Human Context Books.
Russell, G.F.M., Szmuckler, G.I., Dare, C. and Eisler, I. (1987), 'An evaluation of family therapy in anorexia nervosa and bulimia nervosa', *Archives of General Psychiatry*, vol. 444: 1047–56.
Spinelli, E. (1989), *The Interpreted World*, London: Sage.

CHAPTER 6

Duker, M. and Slade, R. (1988), *Anorexia Nervosa and Bulimia: How to Help*, Milton Keynes: Open University Press.

CHAPTER 7

Valère, V. (1978), *Le Pavillon des enfants fous*, Paris: Livre de Poche.

Index